How I Built a 5-HP Stirling Engine

The Story of the Rice Husk Energy Project in Bangladesh

L. Merrick Lockwood

American Stirling Company
2726 Shelter Island Dr. #172
San Diego CA 92106

http://www.stirlingengine.com

How I Built a 5-HP Stirling Engine
Copyright © 2007 American Stirling Company
Printed in United States of America
All rights reserved

Book and Cover design by Michael Crumpton
Cover photograph © L. Merrick Lockwood
Interior photographs and illustrations © L. Merrick Lockwood

Additional copies of this book are available through the following:
Phone: 760-742-2727
Fax: 858-777-3459
Internet: http://www.stirlingengine.com
Email: brent@stirlingengine.com

ISBN 0-9713918-1-5

07 08 09 10 11 • 1 2 3 4 5

ACKNOWLEDGEMENTS

This book describes work carried out as part of the Rice Husk Energy Project in Bangladesh from 1981 to 1986. The project was funded by a grant from the United States Agency for International Development and was implemented by the Asia Foundation in Dhaka. Kumudini Welfare Trust provided the site and some workshop facilities for the project in Narayanganj. Sunpower, Inc. designed and made the project's prototype engine in Athens, Ohio. A number of people became involved in developing the original project proposal and in implementing the project itself. Details of who they were and what they did are given in the following account.

PREFACE

Fairytales usually have happy endings, but only after the reader is led through strange and exciting adventures. A beautiful princess is drugged into perpetual sleep by her jealous stepmother but is brought to life and everlasting happiness by the kiss of a handsome prince. A terrifying, lonely beast is transformed into a wonderful person through the compassion of a sweet and innocent maiden.

The hot air engine started life more than two centuries ago at a time when fairytales were going strong. In its early years it seemed that this engine might have a long and productive existence, but this was not to be, and it settled down for a bit of a snooze. Over the years a number of princes have tried to revive the beast with charm, affection, and a fair bit of dedicated work—perhaps even an occasional kiss. The beast has stirred from time to time, so we know that it is still alive, but the full restoration of the hot air engine to its vibrant and productive self is a dream that is yet to be fulfilled.

This is the story, a true story I might say, of one effort to revive this fascinating beast. For a brief while it stirred and there was a glimmer of hope, but eventually it returned to its slumber. I hope that this account will inspire a prince or a princess to try, with more success, to fully awaken the sleeping beast.

Merrick Lockwood
Shelton Cottage
Lower Shola Road
Kodaikanal, TN 624101
India

CONTENTS

INTRODUCTION

Hot air engines were early competitors with steam engines to provide a source of power that could replace animals, wind mills, and water wheels with more reliable and predictable service. During the 1800s steam engines reigned supreme in applications that required power from 5 hp upwards, but for low-power needs hot air engines were widely used for a diverse range of applications. By the turn of the century, hot air engines were being replaced in these low-power applications by newly developed internal combustion engines and electric motors, and in a few decades they fell almost entirely from practical use.

It had long been recognized that hot air engines had a potential far greater than so far achieved in respect to fuel efficiency and power density. The key to improvements lay in the availability of modern heat-resistant metals, dry lubricating materials, and rolling element bearings, as well as a better understanding of heat and fluid flow processes within the engine. In 1937 the Dutch company Philips launched a program to develop a modern hot air engine to run a small generator that could power the radios the company produced. Philips and others that followed have made giant strides in developing efficient and powerful engines that have become increasingly sophisticated. Eventually, since many engines were charged with helium or hydrogen, the traditional name "hot air engine" had to be abandoned, and they came to be called Stirling engines after Robert Stirling, who patented the first practical engine of this type in 1816.

As Stirling engine development has proceeded, engineers have been under pressure to make them competitive with internal combustion engines in their power-to-weight ratio. The use of exotic gases, high temperatures, and high pressures has resulted in remarkably small and powerful Stirling engines, but ones that are difficult and expensive to manufacture and saddled with durability problems.

Some have suggested from time to time that a well-designed, low-pressure hot air engine made with modern materials would find a ready market in the developing world, where its capability of operating on locally available fuels would be appreciated. The objective of the Rice Husk Energy Project was to

9

develop such an engine.

The Rice Husk Energy Project, which ran from 1981 to 1986, was a project of the Asia Foundation in Bangladesh and was funded by the United States Agency for International Development. The objective of the project was to develop a 5 hp (3.7 kW), low-pressure, air-charged Stirling engine that would operate a small rice mill using rice husk as fuel.

After sketching out the fascinating origins of the hot air engine the following pages document our experience, both failures and successes, in developing the RHEP engines. Perhaps our experiences will inspire as well as caution those who see a bright future for Stirling engines that can be fueled with a range of renewable and waste materials.

Chapter 1
ORIGINS OF HOT AIR ENGINES

As steam engines proliferated in England in the 18th and early 19th centuries, boiler explosions became common occurrences. Frequent newspaper reports recounted incidents that had resulted in fatalities and injuries. One way to avoid boiler explosions was to do away with the boilers by using air rather than water as the working medium. While air engines had been proposed much earlier, it was toward the end of the 1700s and during the 1800s that a number of inventors designed and made functioning hot air engines as alternatives to steam engines.

Two types of hot air engine were developed, open cycle and closed cycle. In open-cycle hot air engines a fresh charge of air is drawn into the working space at the beginning of each cycle. After heating the air to increase its pressure, it is expanded against a piston to generate mechanical power. In some of these engines the air was heated by passing it through a bed of burning fuel; other open-cycle hot air engines used external furnaces that heated the working air through pipes or through the wall of the expansion chamber. While some of these designs were commercialized, they had complicated valve systems, and they were noisy and lacked durability.

Closed-cycle hot air engines contain a fixed charge of air that is confined in the working space by the piston. One part of the working space is maintained at a high temperature by an external furnace, and another part is cooled from the outside by air or water. A displacer shuttles the air within the engine back and forth between the "heater" and the "cooler." When the air is hot (and the pressure is high) it drives the piston through its power stroke; when it is cool (and the pressure is low) the piston compresses the air. This cycle is repeated, sometimes hundreds or thousands of times a minute, to convert the energy from the heated air to mechanical power.

As with steam engines, the development of hot air engines is closely associated with the names of the innovators who developed, introduced, and improved a variety of designs.

Robert Stirling (1790-1878)

Robert Stirling was born on the 25th of October, 1790, at Gloag, Methvin, Perthshire in Scotland. He was one in a line of accomplished inventors and engineers. His grandfather, Michael Stirling, invented the rotary threshing machine. As a boy Robert had an early exposure to machinery from his father, Patrick Stirling, who had himself helped his father, Michael, with his threshing machines. Robert was particularly interested in machinery that produced power.

From 1805 to 1808 Robert studied at Edinburgh University. In November 1809 he enrolled as a student of divinity at Glasgow University and completed five sessions. In November 1814 he continued his divinity studies at Edinburgh University for a year, and in July 1815 he was examined and found competent to preach the gospel. At the age of 26, on September 19, 1816, he was ordained as assistant minister at the Laigh Kirk in Kilmarnock, Ayrshire. Eight days later, on September 27, 1816, Robert Stirling was granted a Scottish patent for his hot air engine with the rather convoluted title, "Improvements for Diminishing the Consumption of Fuel, and in particular an Engine capable of being applied to the moving of Machinery on a Principle entirely new."

The patent described both a closed-cycle hot air engine and an "economizer," which is now referred to as a regenerator. The regenerator stored heat as air flowed from the heater to the cooler and gave this heat back as the air returned from the cooler to the heater. In this way less heat was lost through the cooler, and the fuel efficiency of the engine was significantly improved.

It is likely that Robert had taken courses in science along with his divinity studies. The departments were adjacent to each other, and in later years he donated demonstration models of his engine to the departments of natural philosophy of both universities. In any case it is clear that Robert had a passion for things mechanical

that continued throughout his life.

Robert had probably been working on his engine for several years before moving to Kilmarnock in 1816. In Kilmarnock he met Thomas Morton, who was also interested in new ideas and had his own business. Morton's father was a brick manufacturer, and Thomas had been apprenticed as a turner and wheelwright. At that time, industrial machinery was usually powered by slowly rotating but powerful water wheels, and a system of wooden or metal gears and shafts would be used to increase the speed of rotation and distribute power to a number of machines. Wheelwrights, who were among the most skilled artisans of their day, were responsible for designing and making these elaborate power transmission systems. Thomas Morton arranged for facilities to be built at Morton Place where Robert could carry on his experimental work. This arrangement continued for the next twenty years, even after Robert moved from Kilmarnock to Galston in 1824.

Stirling's patent of September 27, 1816, did not contain details of the patented apparatus. These details, in the form of a "specification," had to be submitted within six months or else the patent would be voided. Four months later, on January 20, 1817, Robert submitted the specifications for his Scottish patent, and it was duly enrolled.

Figure 1.1 has been drawn from illustrations of the engine that appear in Stirling's Scottish patent specifications. The engine had a vertical cylinder that was closed and heated at the top. An inverted walking beam

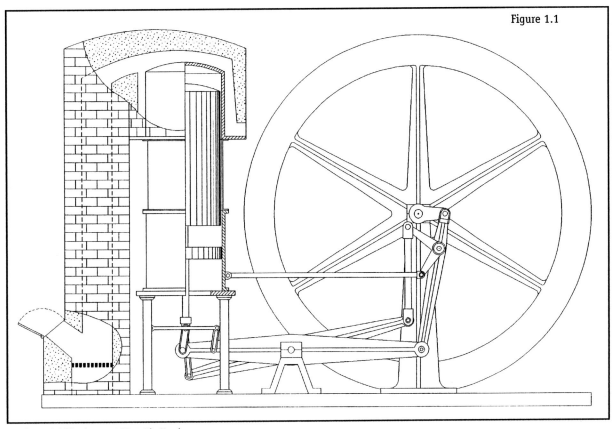

Figure 1.1

Robert Stirling's 1816 Hot Air Engine
Redrawn from figures that appeared in the specifications Robert Stirling submitted for his Scottish patent in 1816. In this engine the piston, which is located at the bottom of the cylinder, is connected to the crankshaft through a Watt parallel-motion linkage and an inverted walking beam. The displacer is located in the upper part of the cylinder and is driven by a separate linkage connected by a rod that passes through the piston. The displacer moves about 90 degrees out of phase with the piston. Brickwork channels combustion gases from the furnace at the lower left, up and around the hot end at the top of the cylinder.

arrangement connected the flywheel to the piston, which was located in the bottom of the cylinder, confining the air inside. From the main connecting rod a separate linkage system drove a rod that passed through the center of the piston and connected to a "displacer." The displacer was a large sealed can loosely fitted in the cylinder that shuttled air within the working space back and forth between the upper hot end and the lower cold end. Regenerator material was wrapped around the displacer, and it was centered in

the cylinder with small rollers mid-way along its length. The displacer moved roughly 90 degrees out of phase with the piston. In this way, when most of the air was in the hot end and the air pressure was high, the piston was in the middle of its expansion stroke, transmitting power to the crankshaft. After the piston reached the bottom of its stroke and started upward through its compression stroke the displacer had shifted the air to the cold end and the pressure was low, requiring little power to compress the air. The cycle was repeated as the displacer again moved the air toward the hot end. One reason that Stirling used an inverted walking beam was to avoid having lubricant for the piston and for the displacer rod migrate to the hot end and become carbonized.

On November 16, 1816, Stirling applied for an English patent, but for reasons that are not clear he did not submit the specifications within the stipulated six-month period, and this patent was voided. One hundred years later, in 1917, as material was gathered to celebrate the centenary of the first Stirling engine, the specifications for the English patent were discovered in poor but legible condition. They were donated to the Patent Office Library and, after being redrawn, were published in *The Engineer* (p. 516) on Dec. 14, 1917.

In 1818 the first full-size air engine based on Stirling's 1816 patent was constructed and used to pump water out of an Ayrshire quarry. The regenerator in this engine was wrapped around and moved with the displacer. This engine was designed to produce 2 hp, and although it didn't achieve this much power, it did function successfully for some time. This was the first closed-cycle air engine put to work.

James Stirling (1800-1876)

Robert Stirling's brother, James, ten years younger, collaborated with Robert in the development of the hot air engine. At the age of thirteen James matriculated at Glasgow and, like his older brother, started studying for the church at Glasgow and Edinburgh. James, however, soon switched to mechanical engineering and was later apprenticed to Claude Girdwood, an engineering firm in Glasgow. In 1816 when Robert was granted his first patent, James was sixteen years old and was certainly already involved with the development of the air engine.

In 1824 James made a proposal of his own. The Ayrshire engine described in the previous section was cooled externally by air or water. This is mentioned in reports, but the drawings do not illustrate just how this was done. The engine was equipped with a Watt "fly ball" governor that controlled an air-release valve in the cylinder, just above the top of the piston's stroke. This valve was activated to prevent the engine from over-speeding when unloaded. Seeing how releasing the pressure of the working air in the engine reduced power, we might surmise that experiments were made to raise the pressure and consequently increase the power. Because the piston was open to the atmosphere, the amount of pressurization would have been limited. This fact led James, in 1824, to propose an engine design that could be pressurized.

After experimenting with working models, Robert and James applied for a second patent in 1827 that included the concept of pressurizing their air engine to increase its power. The arrangement used a double-acting piston ducted to two separate displacers. The displacers, now oriented with the hot end downward, were connected to opposite ends of their own rocking beam so that their weight and the force of pressurization acting on each displacer rod was exactly balanced and exerted no force on the linkage to the flywheel. The regenerators in this design were fixed in the annular space around the displacer. By placing the piston in a cylinder separate from the displacers, it could be lubricated without risk of fouling the regenerator or hot ends with carbonized oil.

James was now working at the engineering firm of Claude Girdwood in Glasgow. In 1828 the brothers' second large engine was fabricated, in which the piston had a diameter of 66 cm (26 inches) and a stroke of 91.5 cm (36 inches). Being double acting, this would give a combined displacement of 626 liters. When this engine was started it produced 15 kW (20 hp), but it lost power as the engine warmed up. The problem was that since the ratio of power to swept volume (and surface area) increased due to pressurization, the previous system of cooling the outside surface of the cylinders was inadequate to cope with the increased flow of heat that had to be rejected by the engine. James quickly realized that a more efficient cooling system was needed, and he abandoned this "Girdwood" engine as he turned his attention to that problem.

A third engine, most likely built in the early 1830s, incorporated the improved cooling system. This engine had a cylinder bore of 9.2 cm (3 5/8 inches), a stroke of 30.5 cm (12 inches), and a swept volume of 2 liters and developed 2 hp. This work led to the Stirling brothers' last patent, granted in 1840, which included, among other things, James's "refrigerating" (water cooling) apparatus. His cooler consisted of a coil of copper tubing filling the space above the regenera-

tor. Water was circulated through the copper tubing, which was in direct contact with the working air to provide efficient cooling.

By this time James was working at the Dundee Foundry of Urquhart Lindsay & Co., first as works engineer and then as manager. The Dundee Foundry was involved in all manner of engineering projects, including water works, docks, and the manufacture of steam locomotives. The brothers' fourth engine incorporating all of their improvements was constructed at the Dundee Foundry and put into operation there to run all of their machinery. This engine had a cylinder bore of 30.5 cm (12 inches), a stroke of 61 cm (24 inches) and a double-acting swept volume of 44.6 liters. It ran at 40 rpm and generated 21 hp (16 kW). It was started in June 1841 and ran all the machinery for eight to ten months. But it was not powerful enough for the requirements of the workshop, so a larger engine was made.

The fifth and last working engine built by Robert and James was similar to but larger than the previous engine and had the following specifications:

This last engine was made by converting an existing steam engine and is illustrated in

• Piston bore	40.6 cm (16 inches)
• Piston stroke	121.9 cm (48 inches)
• Swept vol. (one side)	158 l (9,646 in³)
• Swept vol. (double acting)	316 l (19,292 in³)
• Speed	0.47 Hz (28 rpm)
• Mean working pressure	13.8 bar (200 psi)
• Shaft power	30 kW (40 hp)

Figure 1.2. The vertical double-acting piston was connected upwards to an overhead walking beam to the main connecting rod and crankshaft. A second smaller walking beam supported and operated the two displacers. This smaller walking beam was connected to the crankshaft through a mechanism that could change the stroke length of the displacers while the engine was running.

The engine had an elegant system for governing speed. A Watt fly-ball governor activated the displacer stroke-control mechanism to control engine speed by increasing or decreasing the displacers' length of stroke.

By orienting the piston and displacers vertically, friction losses due to side forces from the weight of these heavy moving parts were eliminated. The working space could easily be pressurized using seals on the displacer rods and the piston rod. Having the piston in a

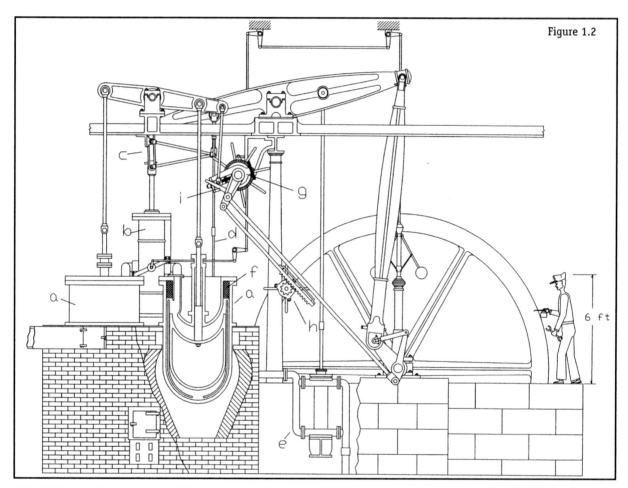

Figure 1.2

The Stirling Brothers Improved Air Engine
The culmination of the Stirling brothers hot air engine development was their 40 hp "Improved Air Engine". This engine powered all the machinery of the Dundee Foundry from March 1843 till December 1845. Engine components included; a) two displacer cylinders, b) double acting power cylinder, c) Watt parallel motion linkage, d) air compressor drive rod, e) cooling water pump, f) regenerator, g) variable stroke mechanism for the displacers controlled by the fly-ball governor, h) manual drive to operate displacers for starting, i) lever to switch displacer drive from manual to engine driven

separate cylinder would result in some losses due to the added dead space in the ducts, but the piston could then be lubricated without the risk of oil contaminating the regenerator or migrating to the hot end.

The annular regenerators were made of thin iron sheets. The coolers were coils of copper tubing within the working space through which cooling water was circulated.

This last Dundee engine was started in March 1843 and satisfactorily powered all the machinery at the Dundee Foundry till December 1845 (two years and nine months), when one hot end burned out. After replacing the hot end the engine ran till May 1846, when the second hot end burned out and was replaced. If we assume that the second hot end had not been replaced at the time of the first repair, this would amount to a life of three years and two months for the second hot end. The third failure occurred eight months later in January 1847, and at this time the company decided to revert to steam power, as the unpredictability of breakdowns with the air engine was unacceptable for a working concern like the Dundee Foundry. Another factor may have been that in 1846 James Stirling had left the Dundee Foundry and moved to Edinburgh, where he took up consulting work. Perhaps the person who succeeded him as manager at the Foundry was not willing to invest the necessary effort and resources to keep the "Improved Air Engine" running.

James Stirling died in 1876 at the age of 75. Robert Stirling survived his younger brother by two years, and in a written tribute to James he included the following prophetic remarks:

"It is a fact then that he almost succeeded in establishing a new mechanical power, which promised to relieve the labours of that gigantic and universal drudge the steam-engine. He constructed at the Dundee Foundry an air-engine which for three years performed all the work of that establishment, and failed at last from imperfections in the material of which it was constructed. These imperfections have been in a great measure removed by time, and especially by the genius of the distinguished Bessemer. If Bessemer iron or steel had been known thirty-five or forty years ago, there is scarce a doubt that the air-engine would have been a great success. But as the nature of cast iron forty years since required the hot part of the engine to be made three times thicker than it would now be, and consequently at least six times less fit for transmitting the heat, the outside of it required to be kept at a much higher temperature than would have been necessary with Bessemer iron . . .

The engine worked to the extent of 40 hp, according to the standard of Watt and Boulton; and this was ascertained not by theoretical calculations, but by proper application of the Trusten strap and movable weights frequently used. Upon the whole, this experiment was conducted with such care and skill; and such jealousy of being deceived, that the result as to power & c., may be considered fully established. It remains for some skilled and ambitious mechanist in a future age to repeat it under more favourable circumstances and with complete success."

Robert would have been even more optimistic had he been able to foresee the future development of stainless steels and other materials that have even more strength and corrosion resistance at high temperatures than Bessemer's steel.

John Ericsson (1803-1889)

John Ericsson was born in Sweden, moved to London in 1826, and then to New York in 1839. Ericsson was a prolific inventor with many successful innovations. He was one of the inventors of the screw propeller, which revolutionized ship propulsion, and he designed and built the Monitor, a Civil War ironclad warship, in a mere 100 working days!

Throughout his working life Ericsson worked on hot air engines. His designs were both closed cycle and open cycle. In open-cycle engines a fresh air charge is drawn in by one piston, heated, expanded with a second piston to derive power, and then exhausted. As these engines incorporated valves they

were more complicated, noisy, and subject to more wear than closed-cycle hot air engines.

Ericsson was able to convince his backers to finance the design and construction, in 1853, of the "Ericsson," a 260-foot-long ship driven by a coal-fired hot air engine. The engine, which ran at 9 rpm, had 4 cylinders, each with a bore of 14 feet and stroke of 6 feet, certainly the biggest hot air engine ever made! Unfortunately the ship was not a success.

Ericsson persisted, and after many unsuccessful designs he developed an open-cycle engine that was manufactured and successfully marketed in sizes with bores from 8 inches up to 32 inches.

Around 1872 John Ericsson designed a successful closed-cycle hot air engine. It was intended to be used along the American Pacific coast to pump irrigation water using a solar concentrator as a heat source. Though this heating arrangement was not successful, it was eventually patented in 1880 as a pumping engine that could be fueled by coal, wood, or gas. This engine was manufactured with bores from 5 inches up to 12 inches and was in widespread use at the turn of the century. The configuration of this engine was similar to Stirling's 1816 patent, with piston and displacer in one cylinder but with the hot end oriented downward. The linkage Ericsson used with this engine consisted of a crankshaft with a single throw that connected both to the piston and through a bell crank to the displacer. A modified version of this "Ericsson" linkage was used in the prototype as well as the first and second intermediate models of the Rice Husk Energy Project engine described in this book.

Philips Stirling engines (1937-1980)

In the Netherlands the Philips Company, an electronics and lamp-manufacturing firm, wanted to make a small generator to power radios in areas where no grid electricity was available. To this end, in 1937, the Philips Radio Factory discussed with H. Rinia and J. Haantjes of the firm's research laboratory the possibility of developing a small generator of a few tens of watts. In March 1938 H. de Brey joined Rinia and Haantjes and investigated a wide variety of power sources that might be used to drive the small generator. He concluded that the hot air engine held the most promise for a silent and durable power plant. Added advantages were that it would not generate radio interference from an ignition system and it could be fueled with widely available kerosene. Later that year de Brey located and bought a small hot air engine in Germany, which was carefully tested and found to have a relatively miserable performance, presumably offering the scope for much improvement.

After analyzing the shortcomings of earlier hot air engines, de Brey designed a little engine that incorporated several improvements in the heater, the cooler, and the regenerator (in which he used matted 0.03 mm wire). This very first Philips engine, the Type 1 (Fig. 1.3), performed exceptionally well. With a bore of 30 mm, stroke of 25 mm and displacement of 17.7 cm³ the engine produced 16 watts at 1,000 rpm. This perfor-

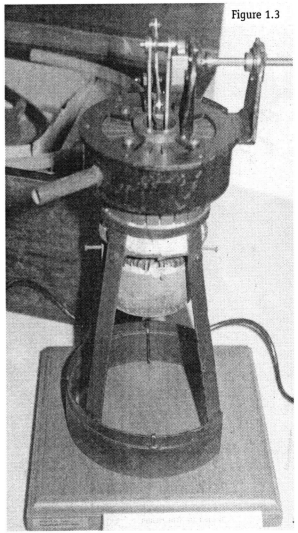

Figure 1.3

First Stirling engine by Philips, 1938
The "Type 1" engine embodied many improvements to the design of a commercially available model engine of similar size evaluated by the Philips team. This engine, with a swept volume of 17.7 cm3, produced 16 watts at 1,000 rpm, clearly demonstrating the scope for improving the performance of Stirling engines.

mance of close to 1 watt/cm³ swept volume in an un-pressurized air engine is a remarkable achievement even by today's standards. The Type 1 engine is also interesting since its mechanical configuration is similar to Robert Stirling's first engine and almost identical to the first three engines made in the Rice Husk

Energy Project. This arrangement—piston and displacer in one cylinder (beta configuration) with a single throw crank driving the piston directly and the displacer through a bell crank—was used in several Philips engines.

In the following years Philips carried out the first pioneering work to develop a modern hot air engine. When helium, hydrogen, and nitrogen began to be used as alternatives to air as the working medium, the people at Philips adopted the term "Stirling engine." Toward the end of the 1940s the transistor was invented, paving the way for radios that could run for long periods on a few inexpensive flashlight batteries. The "small" generator of a few watts capacity was no longer needed and had, in the meantime, grown into a 200-watt general-purpose generator. This generator used the Type 10 engine that had been developed in 1941-42. The Type 10 engine had a swept volume of 64 cm^3, incorporated a built-in compressor to raise air pressure inside the engine to 5 bar, and was capable of producing 500 watts of shaft power at 1500 rpm. This engine, coupled with a 200-watt generator, was designated the "bungalow set."

In 1951 a Dutch firm, Johan de Witt, started a manufacturing run of 250 units of the final version of this generator set, the 102C. In the end 150 sets were produced before it was decided that the generator would be too costly to be competitive. A larger 1,000-watt "Type 117" generator set was deemed to be marketable but only with an investment in the range of a million dollars. Such funds were not available

at that time since Philips was concentrating all of its resources on the mass production of television. The bottom line: Philips was an electronics firm, not an engine manufacturer. In 1953 the Engines Division, formed just two years earlier, was disbanded.

Just a month before the demise of the Engines Division Rolf J. Meijer was given the task of designing a small Stirling-powered generator of a few watts output to power a radio, representing the original objective of Philips' Stirling engine program. This set would be presented to H. Rinia as a gift when he celebrated the completion of twenty-five years with the Philips Company. Over a weekend Meijer conceived and designed a completely new drive mechanism incorporating two crankshafts that made it possible to perfectly balance a single cylinder engine. Within four weeks this "rhombic drive" engine was made, coupled to a small generator and radio, and was ready for presentation to Rinia on November 11, 1953. The rhombic engine impressed everyone present, including Fritz J. Philips. Although the Engines Division was still dissolved within a month, the Research Lab began to actively pursue the development of the rhombic drive engine.

A number of remarkable rhombic drive engines emerged from the work at Philips and in collaboration with other groups. The US military was interested in a small and silent generator, so, in the early 1960s, General Motors produced the single cylinder 3 kW GPU (Ground Power Unit). In 1967 Philips started work on their 4-235 engine (4 cylinders with 235 cm³ per cylinder). In 1971 this 117 kW (157 hp) rhombic drive engine was installed in a bus by the Dutch firm DAF to demonstrate the potential of Stirling engines for use in automotive applications with very low levels of emissions.

The remarkable balance and absence of vibration in the rhombic drive was demonstrated with the large 4-cylinder 360-15 engine. In this case the numbers refer to the power (360 hp) and the speed (1,500 rpm). There was so little vibration in this engine that a polygonal British coin placed upright on the crankcase would remain standing even with the engine running at full power.

In later years, attention shifted from the rhombic drive to double-acting engines with swash plate drives. Swash plate engines are more compact and would be cheaper to mass produce than rhombic engines, and they have been used, or are in use, in sophisticated applications such as motor vehicles and solar power plants. However, for me and many other Stirling engine enthusiasts, the rhombic engine is the key to a really durable working engine, particularly for use with alternative fuels in rural areas of the world where fossil fuels are expensive and scarce.

• • • • •

Rice husk as a fuel

Rice is the most widely consumed cereal crop in the world. The rice kernel is surrounded and protected by a tough covering called the husk or hull, which represents about 20 percent of the weight of paddy. Unlike other cereal grains such as wheat, rice husk is not removed during threshing, and the paddy with its husk intact is bagged, transported, and stored. Before rice can be cooked and consumed it must be milled to remove the inedible husk. In the milling process, part or all of the outer bran layer is also removed.

The energy content of rice husk is somewhat less than other biomass because of its high content of silica, but it still represents a very significant potential source of energy. Typical values of energy content of rice husk and some fuels are as follows:

- Rice husk   13 mJ/kg
- Wood   18 mJ/kg
- Coal   30 mJ/kg
- Kerosene   46 mJ/kg

Bangladesh has produced up to twenty million tons of paddy a year. The husk from this paddy amounts to four million tons with an energy content of 52 giga-Joules (gJ). The energy available from this rice husk is thus equivalent to over a billion liters of diesel fuel each year.

Husk-fueled rice mills

The utility of rice husk as a fuel for providing mechanical power has been quite well exploited, but only on a relatively large scale. In Bangladesh, eighty steam-powered rice mills were operating in the early 1980s. Most of these mills were using steam engines purchased from tea estates as those operations switched from wood fuel to grid power.

In a typical installation, a Lancashire

21

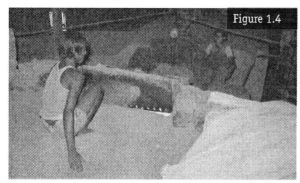

The Lancashire boiler is fitted with a step-grate furnace. Rice husk is scattered by hand through a narrow gap onto the step grate of the furnace.

boiler is equipped with a step-grate furnace that is continuously fed from above by hand, scattering the husk through a narrow horizontal aperture (Fig. 1.4). A tall chimney provides the draft to draw combustion air through the step grate and the boiler tubes. Boilers are typically operated at low pressures, 50-90 psi, so a steam engine like that shown in Figure 1.5, which might be capable of 200 hp, would operate at only 40-50 hp. This is enough, however, to run the rice milling machinery in a reasonably large mill, and no electricity is used except for a few light bulbs.

Rice is usually soaked, parboiled, and re-dried before it is milled. In Figure 1.6 workers transfer paddy from the soaking tank to the parboiling tank. Exhaust steam from the engine is piped into the parboiling tank for five to ten minutes to heat the paddy to the boiling point. Figure 1.7 shows how the parboiled rice is unloaded and then spread in the drying yard (Fig. 1.8) to sun dry before it is milled.

These large rice mills powered by the waste husk from the milling operation inspired the idea of developing similar machinery, but on a small scale, for rural rice mills in countries like Bangladesh.

The steam engine along with the boiler and all the auxiliaries was purchased from a tea estate in northeast Bangladesh that was converting from steam to electric power from the national grid. The purchaser paid only for the scrap value of the metal of the steam plant.

Figure 1.6

After soaking for a day or two till it is saturated, the paddy (rough rice) is transferred to the parboiling tanks.

Figure 1.7

Exhaust steam from the mill's engine is piped into the tanks for 10 to 15 minutes to parboil the soaked paddy, which is then removed from below.

Figure 1.8

The parboiled paddy is sun dried and then milled to yield the finished rice that may be cooked and consumed.

Chapter 2

DEVELOPING THE RHEP PROPOSAL

(August 1979–June 1981)

In December of 1978 I was at an evening social gathering in Dhaka, firmly gripping a glass of beer while I searched for someone with whom I wouldn't have to make polite conversation. After a bit I spied Jim Dillard, the Asia Foundation representative in Bangladesh, and made my way through the crowd to chat with him.

As it happened, Jim had recently been thinking that he would like to take up a project that was different from the usual Asia Foundation activities. TAF's typical activities centered on library development, book distribution, strengthening legal structures, facilitating professional development in the USA, and organizing other scholarly exchanges. So when we met that evening Jim asked if I had any ideas for an "interesting" project. This shifted my conversational ability into high gear, and I deluged Jim with a stream of ideas related to rural technology. It was all a bit too much for that time in the evening, so Jim suggested that I write up a one-page outline of the one project that I thought would be most interesting and useful and come by his office the next day to discuss it.

In June of 1979 I would be completing four years as Adviser on Appropriate Agricultural Technology with the Bangladesh Agricultural Research Council (BARC). During this time I had a chance to observe a number of interesting rural technologies. One of the most fascinating for me was represented by a few of the big rice mills in Bangladesh that used the energy available in rice husks as the source of power to run the mills. In these mills, husk-fueled boilers powered large steam engines that drove all the machinery in the mill through a line shaft. There was, however, no technology available at the time for powering small rice mills with the energy from rice husks. A day or so after my talk with Jim, I went to the Asia Foundation with the outline of a project to develop and introduce a rice husk–fueled engine for small rice mills in rural Bangladesh.

Jim was enthusiastic about the idea, and we began to look in detail at the prospects for such a project. We came up with the arrangement that after completing my stint with BARC and returning to the USA, I would return to Bangladesh as a consultant to the Asia Foundation for a few months to prepare a proposal for a Rice Husk Energy Project.

The objective of the proposed project was to develop and introduce a 5-hp rice husk–fueled engine that could power the smallest of the conventional steel (Engleberg) rice hullers commonly used in Bangladesh. As the project proposal was developed, we addressed two additional concerns. The first related to the impact of mechanized rice milling on women's employment; the second to the alternative uses for rice husk and the effect of these demands on the availability of husk for use as fuel to power a rice mill.

I was responsible for preparing the Rice Husk Energy Project proposal, which would be submitted to the United States Agency for International Development (USAID) by the Asia Foundation. It seemed pretty straightforward. We would take a few months to prepare the project proposal, the Asia Foundation would submit it to USAID, and they would say "yes" or "no."

We did prepare and submit the proposal within a few months, but the response from USAID was neither "yes" nor "no" but "perhaps." We were asked to address one issue related to the project and resubmit the proposal. We repeated this exercise several times, and in the end it took almost two years to get final approval of the project proposal.

The Asia Foundation had no history of dealing with projects relating to engineering, but the foundation had a close working relationship with Kumudini Welfare Trust, a Hindu philanthropic organization based in the town of Narayanganj, fifteen miles south of Dhaka. There were two reasons for the involvement of Kumudini Welfare Trust in the Rice Husk Energy Project. The first was the dynamic character of the director, Mrs. Pati, who had diversified the activities of Kumudini Welfare Trust and developed contacts with many international organizations, among them the Asia Foundation. The second reason was that KWT had a large, though somewhat antiquated, workshop that was used to

maintain the tug boats of the Bengal River Service and four huge hydraulic presses for baling jute. These presses had been erected in the 1800s, the oldest in 1881. The KWT workshop had a lot of "down time" between hectic periods when a press broke down or one of the BRS tug boats needed repairs. The plan was for the workshop to work on our engine during these periods of slack activity. Ultimately this arrangement turned out to be inefficient, and the Rice Husk Energy Project eventually had its own complete workshop.

In 1978 I had been responsible, on behalf of Bangladesh Agricultural Research Council, for organizing a task force to look at the utilization of by-products from rice processing in Bangladesh. Funding and some experts for the task force were provided by the Food and Agricultural Organization of the United Nations. The resource person for rice husk as an energy source was Eldon Beagle, who was just finishing his landmark work "Rice Husk Conversion to Energy," which came out a year later in 1979 as FAO's Agricultural Services Bulletin No. 31.

Eldon was a goldmine of information on different ways to generate mechanical power from the energy in rice husks and was always ready to share his knowledge freely. At this time we discussed the prospects for a small rice husk–powered rice mill and the type of prime movers that might be used. These possibilities included steam power, rice husk gasification, and rice husk–fueled Stirling engines. In October 1980 Eldon returned to Dhaka on a one-week consultancy with the Asia Foundation to strengthen the rice husk/energy side of the latest revision of the proposal. Once the project was approved, Eldon continued as a consultant for the project till, very sadly, he passed away in 1983.

William Beale carried out pioneering work on free piston Stirling engines while he was teaching mechanical engineering at Ohio University in Athens, Ohio. In 1971 he set up Sunpower, Inc. to develop and commercialize these concepts. William had written about the potential for biomass-fueled Stirling engines in a booklet on renewable energy resources that I had come across, so I wrote asking him if he thought it was feasible to power a small rice mill with a rice husk–fueled Stirling engine. The answer, in short, was "yes."

More correspondence followed, and when I returned to the USA in the summer of 1979 I had a chance to visit Sunpower in Ohio. At that time the Asia Foundation arranged to bring William to Bangladesh for a week in October. This visit would enable him to see the kind of small rice mill we wanted to power with rice husks, and he would help us prepare the technical component of our project proposal. Because no project was yet approved, William agreed to come even though only his travel and accommodations were provided. I took William to see the Kumudini Welfare Trust facilities in Narayanganj, and in the next three days we packed in several meetings and excursions to remote country rice mills. In a whirlwind three-day trip we flew to Calcutta and took a train to Kharagpur to visit the Indian Institute of Technology, where a

group was working on cyclone husk furnaces. In the end William's technical input to the proposal was critical for its eventual approval, and the cyclone furnace designed for the Rice Husk Energy Project by Sunpower incorporated elements from the Kharagpur work.

Within the United States Agency for International Development (USAID) there was a range of enthusiasm and skepticism as we worked to get the proposal approved. Predictably, their agricultural engineer, Dan Jenkins, was very supportive. When we got together I would carry on about the marvels of a biomass-fueled Stirling engine while he listened with interest. The director of USAID, Frank Kimball, was much less enthusiastic. Apparently he had backed an "appropriate technology" project at an earlier posting, and when the project had fizzled Frank was left holding the bag. He didn't want to get his fingers burned a second time. When the project was finally approved, Frank insisted that everyone who endorsed it had to sign off on the document.

The key person in USAID for me was Ingrid Buxell, who was responsible for Private Voluntary Organization (PVO) activities. It was only due to Ingrid's encouragement and prodding that all the necessary paperwork got done. Later, during the course of the project, a number of different USAID staff were involved in monitoring and evaluating our work. I think most of them quite enjoyed the chance to be involved in a different sort of activity and were intrigued by the gadget that we were developing.

• • • • •

There are a number of ways in which the energy from rice husks could be used to power a rice mill. Of these, three were considered for this project:

1. Rice husk–fired steam boiler with engine
2. Rice husk gasifier with IC engine
3. Rice husk–fueled Stirling engine

Using steam power to run large rice mills is well established around the world. In Bangladesh, according to the records of the Government's Chief Boiler Inspector, there were eighty large steam-powered rice mills operating in 1979. There are some disadvantages to these mills, however. The large amount of metal used in making this equipment means that the present-day cost of manufacturing them would be beyond the scope of most mills. Another disadvantage is that it is only economical to start one of these mills if there is a suitably large batch of rice to process, typically 100 tons or more. Most of the rice mills in Bangladesh could not make use of a milling capacity this large. The scope for a small steam-powered rice mill would be quite good except for the intricacies and cost of boiler licensing and operation, which would be difficult for the owner of a small rural mill to achieve.

Gasifiers were common during World War II, when fossil fuels were in short supply. In Italy, rice-husk gasifiers were used to run rice mills until recently, so the technology has been fully developed. The disadvantages with gasifiers are the complexity and cost of equipment. In addition to having the equipment needed to gasify the rice husk and clean the gas, it is necessary to operate and maintain the internal combustion engine that it powers. For a 5-hp mill this would likely be an excessively complex and expensive arrangement.

Stirling engines had the disadvantage that recent developments in the field had been directed more at high-tech applications such as solar power and automotive propulsion. At that time there was no off-the-shelf Stirling engine that suited the needs of a small rice mill. Their advantage, however, was that they represented the simplest way to convert the energy of rice husk into mechanical power. The husk could be burned in a furnace to heat the engine without the need for boilers or gas cleaners. Because of the potential offered by Stirling engines, we selected this technology for the Rice Husk Energy Project.

The much revised proposal was finally approved by USAID director Frank Kimball on June 10, 1981, On June 22nd the project document was co-signed by USAID acting director Larry Crandall and the Asia Foundation's newly appointed representative, Ian McCabe. The title of the document was "ENERGY FROM RICE HUSKS, 1981-1984 (TAF/Rice: 388-0045-07)." We called it the "Rice Husk Energy Project," and it commenced July 1, 1981.

Initially the project consisted of three phases of one year each. Sunpower, Inc. would be subcontracted by the Asia Foundation to design and fabricate the prototype engine in Phase 1. The budget for the three phases of the project was $925,737, of which $240,000 was earmarked for Sunpower's fees for the design and fabrication of the prototype during Phase 1 and for follow-up support in Phase 2 and Phase 3.

Provision was made for a number of consultants to support the project. Eldon Beagle visited Sunpower seven times as the prototype engine was being designed and fabricated in Phase 1 to provide technical backup on the development of the furnace design and participate in four design reviews. He also arranged for rice husk to be supplied from Louisiana for use as fuel. Eldon was scheduled to participate in evaluations twice a year in Bangladesh during Phase 2 and Phase 3. Dr. Graham (Joe) Walker from the University of Calgary provided the Asia Foundation with an independent evaluation of the Stirling engine and participated in the four technical reviews during Phase 1. As Project Manager I also attended these reviews, the first at the start of the project, then after four months, eight months, and the all-important final review at the end of Phase 1. The final technical review would determine if funding for Phase 2 of the Rice Husk Energy Project would be released to the Asia Foundation by USAID.

Kumudini Welfare Trust's contribution to the project included workshop space and office facilities as well as some staff support. At the end of the project Kumudini would retain all the equipment and materials procured for the project to assist them in developing a production and marketing facility for the project's engine.

In the past, rice processing was carried out using manual methods and was exclusively women's activity, a laborious and not very profitable activity at that. Mechanized rice milling is very profitable, but invariably it is men who own these mills and men who operate and maintain the diesel engines used for power in rural areas where there is no electricity supply. We hoped to demonstrate that a small rice mill powered by a rice husk–fueled Stirling engine would enable women to engage in, and profit from, the business of mechanized rice milling. To assist us in addressing these gender-related issues we had the assistance of Shireen Huq as a consultant who had extensive experience in matters relating to women's activities in Bangladesh.

What we expected to accomplish was outlined in the anticipated outputs of the three phases.

Phase 1: Output

A prototype rice husk–fueled engine made by Sunpower in the USA with the following criteria:

- The engine should produce 5 hp (3.7 kW)
- The engine should be fueled by rice husk
- The quantity of husk consumed should not be more than that produced during the milling operation
- It should be possible to manufacture the engine in Bangladesh with existing workshop facilities.

In Bangladesh we were to set up a workshop facility and confirm through surveys that small rice mills benefited most women in rural areas and that husk would be available to fuel the mill.

Phase 2: Output

After making necessary design changes, four intermediate rice husk–fueled engines would be made at the RHEP facility and field tested.

Phase 3: Output

After final design changes, we would build four preproduction engines in local workshops and field test them. Finally, the design of the rice husk–fueled Stirling engine would be released to any interested manufacturer. It was intended that no patented features would be used in the engine design so that it could be distributed freely to interested parties.

As the project progressed it became clear that these objectives were overly optimistic, and subsequently we set more realistic targets.

In July of 1981 the Asia Foundation finalized its subcontract with Sunpower for the design and fabrication of the prototype RHEP engine. At this time the people at Sunpower were worried that we might jump the gun and release the design of the engine before it was adequately field tested and proven to be durable. Their concern was that a highly touted Stirling engine that failed to live up to expectations would give all Stirling engines a bad name and would be a setback to other efforts to commercialize the technology. To this end they insisted that someone in the San Francisco office of the Asia Foundation sign an undertaking that we would not release the design of the rice husk–fueled Stirling engine until it was thoroughly field tested and proven. In retrospect we see a bit of irony in this exercise. Before our project was over, Sunpower had spun off a new company, Stirling Technology, Inc., which collaborated with Stirling Dynamics in India to manufacture an engine based on the RHEP prototype design. At the very end of our project we finally, and rather belatedly, abandoned the problematic Ericsson linkage of the prototype for a more robust Ross linkage. This finally gave us a very durable and promising engine, but by this time our project funds were exhausted. In the meantime the US/Indian consortium was well along toward commercial production of a modified version of the prototype engine with the Ericsson linkage. The design of this engine, the ST-5, incorporated a fix to solve the linkage problems but after time and wear there were inevitable failures. Although the ST-5 did not prove to be the durable workhorse that could be used in rural areas of the third world, it did demonstrate the prospects of a biomass-fueled Stirling engine to the world.

Chapter 3

RHEP PHASE 1

(July 1981–August 1982)

The key component of Phase 1 was the design and fabrication of the prototype rice husk–fueled Stirling engine by Sunpower, Inc. in Athens, Ohio. The release of funds for Phase 2 was contingent on the successful demonstration of the prototype by Sunpower at their facility by the end of Phase 1.

While work on the prototype engine was underway in the USA a number of activities were taken up in Bangladesh. A project site on the premises of Kumudini Welfare Trust was made ready, and two lingering issues from discussions with USAID relating to husk utilization and women's employment were addressed. As the prototype engine took shape in Ohio I studied the design and planned how we would make the different parts in Bangladesh.

Making the prototype

Sunpower's area of specialization was, and still is, free piston Stirling machines. By 1979 Sunpower had developed considerable experience in the design of free piston Stirling engines, including computer simulations that aided in these designs. While Sunpower's focus was on free piston engines, they had at that time recently completed a project for Briggs & Stratton to develop a 1-hp Stirling engine with a kinematic (mechanical) drive. The result of this exercise was a rather neat propane-fired rhombic drive engine that stood waist high and happily

pumped considerable quantities of water. If they had shown this engine to farmers in Bangladesh or India it would have caused great excitement, and innovative ways would soon have been devised to fuel it with agricultural residues. Briggs & Stratton, however, is renowned for the mass production of small engines with high power-to-weight ratios, and apparently the thought of a hefty 1-hp engine standing waist high was beyond contemplation for them, so work on this interesting engine stopped.

For the Rice Husk Energy Project the prospect of a bulky 5-hp engine was not a serious problem. Slow-speed diesel engines used in some rice mills were so bulky that they had to be transported in pieces and erected on site, and these still required a fossil fuel.

At Sunpower the team that worked on the prototype was headed by William Beale; Bruce Chagnot was the project engineer; Gary Wood developed the kinematic design; and Larry Penswick was responsible for the thermal design. For a period during November and December of 1981, Bruce visited Dhaka, and I showed him the facilities available for fabricating machinery and the range of hardware, materials, and tools that could be procured locally. As there was some doubt at Sunpower whether the No. 4 steel huller actually required a full 5 hp for its operation, Bruce brought a torque-indicating pulley and stroboscopic tachometer

31

The engine shed under construction in front of the entrance to the project site and the worker's toilet and bathing facility

A row of rooms converted to provide office and laboratory space, a rice mill, and a storeroom. In front is the drying yard.

to accurately measure the power used by these mills. We carried out tests in the RHEP pilot rice mill and at some small commercial mills, where we confirmed that the No. 4 huller does indeed use the full 5 hp available from the diesel engines that power them.

One constraint on the design of the prototype engine was our desire not to use any patented features in the engine so that the design, if successful, could be freely disseminated without becoming entangled in issues relating to intellectual property rights. The engine design that Sunpower developed had the following features:

- Piston and displacer in one cylinder (beta configuration)
- Ericsson linkage, single throw crank with articulated linkage to the piston and bell crank drive for the displacer
- Displacer TDC leads piston TDC ....68.6 degrees
- Piston and displacer bore........................300 mm
- Piston stroke..................................100 mm
- Displacer stroke..............................96 mm
- Piston swept volume.........................7,065 cm^3
- Regenerator of knitted 0.004 SS wire (Metex)..........4 kg
- Operating speed.............................720 rpm
- Working fluid/pressure........................air/4.5 bar
- Cyclone rice husk furnace

The engine was not equipped with a governor.

Sunpower reasoned that the speed would be limited by the rapid increase in flow friction as the seven liters of air was shuttled back and forth by the displacer. As it turned out, the heavy load on the displacer linkage was the most serious problem we had to deal with during the project.

The project site was located on the premises of Kumudini Welfare Trust at Narayanganj, an industrial town and river port located 15 miles south-east of Dhaka. Kumudini Welfare Trust had provided a few acres of land on which there was a large warehouse and a row of storage rooms. The warehouse eventually became a spacious workshop, and the store rooms were converted to provide us with a reception room, an office, a laboratory and a pilot rice mill powered by a diesel engine. In the center of the yard, facilities for parboiling and sun drying paddy were constructed, along with an open shed where the rice husk–fueled engines would be set up for testing. A well was drilled for water and electrical connections made throughout the facility. Bathing and toilet facilities were constructed, and a

The large warehouse converted into a spacious workshop for the project

Transferring soaked paddy to the parboiling drums

boundary wall and gate were erected for security (Figures 3.1, 3.2, 3.3).

During June of 1982, I purchased a lathe, drill press, milling machine, sheet-metal shear and sheet-metal rolling machine. Welding equipment and a variety of hand tools had been ordered earlier from the United States. Our idea was that most of the machining would be done in the main Kumudini Welfare Trust workshop, which had half a dozen lathes of various sizes as well as a large milling machine and some other equipment. Many of these were old machines driven from overhead line shafts. Though they would have made wonderful museum pieces, they were fully functional. Later as the project got going, the limitations of our original plan became obvious and we decided to fully equip the project's workshop.

Workers for the Rice Husk Energy Project were seconded from the main KWT workshop. Their regular salary, paid by Kumudini, was covered by the project. The additional benefit they got through the project was extra pay for any overtime work. This arrangement worked wonderfully, as we ended up many days working long hours, which they were happy to do. During most of the project I had six workshop staff, including two turners (lathe operators), a drill/milling machine man, a welder, a fitter, and an assistant.

Pilot rice mill

We set up and operated the diesel-powered rice mill for three reasons: first, to familiarize ourselves with small-scale rice processing; second, to provide a supply of rice husk for the project; and third, to demonstrate the feasibility of women operating a small rice mill. Four women day-laborers who had been involved with the renovation of the project facilities were hired to operate the mill, and a fifth woman who had completed secondary school was appointed to manage the mill.

In Bangladesh most of the rice is parboiled. Parboiling involves soaking the paddy till it is saturated (a day or two), steaming it, and then drying it in the sun. For the pilot rice mill, soaking was done in large clay "charas" (Fig. 3.4). The soaked rice with a little water was put in a half oil drum and heated over an open fire till steam emerged from the

Figure 3.5

Using wood and rice husk as fuel to parboil the soaked paddy

Figure 3.6

After parboiling, the paddy is sun dried.

top (Fig. 3.5). Finally the paddy was spread in a thin layer on the cement yard to dry in the sun (Fig. 3.6). Parboiling seals cracks in the rice kernel and makes it tough. This reduces breakage during milling and gives a higher yield of unbroken rice. Parboiled rice is also superior to conventional "raw" rice in respect to nutrition. Minerals and vitamins from the bran layers soak into the starchy kernel so that even when fully polished to remove the bran, parboiled rice retains some of the nutrients of brown rice.

In Bangladesh there are three sizes of steel huller commonly used for milling rice. The No. 4 huller is the smallest and requires 5-10 hp; the middle-sized No. 8 huller requires 10-15 hp. The largest steel huller needs 20-30 hp, but by some obscure twist of logic it is designated as a No. 2 huller. An objective of

the project was to develop the smallest commercially viable rice husk–fueled rice mill, so it was a No. 4 huller that we installed in the rice mill. The installation shown in Figures 3.7, 3.8 and 3.9 is typical of small rice mills in which a 5-hp diesel engine drives the steel huller with a flat belt.

During Phase 1 Eldon Beagle, the Asia Foundation's consultant on rice husk, made frequent visits to Sunpower to provide technical backup on the design of rice husk furnace. Eldon also arranged for the supply of rice husk from Louisiana used in the development of the furnace and for the test runs. Dr. Graham Walker from University of Calgary was the Asia Foundation's consultant who would provide us with an independent evaluation the Stirling engine itself. I visited Sunpower four times while work on the prototype proceeded. My second visit was in January 1982 and involved a bit of unwanted drama that had a long-term impact on the project.

Not long after he signed the Rice Husk Energy Project agreement with USAID in June 1981, Ian McCabe left the Asia Foundation. By the end of 1981 Jim Novak had been designated to be the new representative for the Asia Foundation in Bangladesh. It would be a while before Jim could take up his duties in Dhaka, but since he lived in Pennsylvania, not far from Athens, the Asia Foundation head office in San Francisco suggested that he sit in on the review at Sunpower in January 1982 to familiarize himself with the Rice Husk Energy Project. Initially I thought this was a great idea but was soon to change my mind. Jim had been involved at some point with a project to set up a chemical plant, where detailed drawings of the whole facility had to be finalized before ground was broken. Expecting to see the final design of our engine down to the last detail, Jim was chagrined to find that the drawings were undergoing changes even as fabrication of the prototype engine proceeded. No amount of reassuring that designing an engine was different from building a chemical plant satisfied Jim, and for a while I feared that the whole project would be scuttled. During one of Novak's tirades William Beale quietly got up and walked out of the meeting room, turning the meeting over to his staff. From that moment on William declined to even be in the same room as Jim Novak. At one point William was on the verge of returning the Asia Foundation's money and calling it quits, but in the end the work continued.

There were long-term ramifications of Novak's aggressive approach to Sunpower. William Beale, as team leader for Sunpower, and Bruce Chagnot were to have traveled to Bangladesh every six months

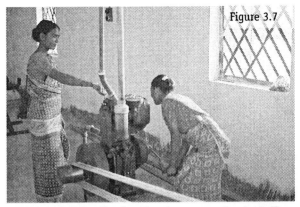
Figure 3.7
Starting the 5-hp diesel engine that powers the rice huller

Figure 3.8
As the rice is milled, husk and bran pass to the rear of the huller.

Figure 3.9
Milled rice flows from the front of the No. 4 steel huller

for the next two years to provide us with technical backup. Now William delegated his responsibility to Craig Kinzelman, one of Sunpower's administrative staff. As the project progressed it became clear that the mechanical linkages in the engine, particularly the displacer drive, were not strong enough. Bruce, however, was adamant that the prototype design was adequate, and as he represented the Sunpower design team, Jim Novak wasn't even willing to discuss the possibility of modifying or changing the linkage design. It wasn't until January of 1986, four years later, after the Asia Foundation had a new representative in Bangladesh, that William Beale, along with Rod Fauvel from the University of Calgary, came out to Dhaka for the final design review of the project. While this resulted in a new and promising design, there was not enough time remaining in the project to fully demonstrate this engine's potential. But we are getting ahead of ourselves here.

Prototype demonstration in Ohio (August 1982)

As I said earlier, funding for each phase of the Rice Husk Energy Project was dependent on the successful completion of the prior phase. The success of the prototype demonstration by Sunpower would determine whether or not the project would continue with the release of funding for Phase 2. In addition to Sunpower staff and me, participants in the evaluation included Doris Bebb from the Asia Foundation's head office in San Francisco and our two consultants,

Eldon Beagle and Graham Walker.

I had arrived in Athens, Ohio, on August 15, two days before the start of the final technical review and demonstration of the RHEP prototype engine. On Monday the 16th I was on hand for an early trial run. At this stage the auxiliaries had not been integrated with the engine. The furnace blower and the compressor to pressurize the air within the engine were electrically powered, and the cooling water was supplied from the water mains. Rice husk had been shipped in from Louisiana for use as fuel and, as it was not feasible to operate a small rice mill in Ohio, the engine drove a water pump through a torque meter (Fig. 3.10). A computerized data-logging system monitored temperatures, speed, and torque. These parameters along with the power output were continuously displayed by means of digital readouts. It was exciting to see the dream realized—a rice husk–fueled engine churning out more than 5 hp in the form of a torrent of water through a 4-inch hose that would do a fire truck proud (Fig. 3.11). By that evening the other participants in the evaluation had arrived—Eldon Beagle from California, Graham Walker from Canada, and Doris Bebb from TAF headquarters in San Francisco.

Tuesday, August 17 was day one of the evaluation. After an initial meeting we adjourned to the test area, which had been designated "Dacca West," where the engine was ready to be started. The cyclone furnace worked well but didn't have the capacity to run the engine steadily at the maximum power of over 5 hp. In order to test the limits of the engine it would be operated at a low speed while the electric blower and husk feed were operated at full blast. This

Bruce works with the prototype engine the day before the August 1982 demonstration in Ohio. The transducer in the foreground measures torque for power calculations.

William leans against the force of water being pumped by the prototype engine.

heated up the thermal mass in the walls of the furnace as well as the hot end of the engine. After a period of this "heat soaking," the engine would be allowed to speed up, and for some minutes its upper power limits could be monitored. Using this routine the previous day, the engine had produced over 5 hp, but on this most critical day the engine was not performing well and the maximum power output registered was less than 3 hp. The reason for the poor performance was revealed when we opened the engine and found that the main con rod had cracked. Back in the meeting room, Graham Walker had to note that the result of day one was a "no go" for Phase 2.

The problem now was that there was no spare main con rod ready, though there was a steel casting. Thus started a crash program that carried on till 2:30 the next morning to machine a replacement main connecting rod.

By the time we assembled on the second day of the evaluation the main connecting rod had been replaced, the engine had been reassembled, and we were back at "Dacca West" for the second trial run. Graham Walker, whose concern was the Stirling engine itself, had earlier jotted down a suggested test protocol that included a number of start-up and shut-down cycles and full power operation for an extended period. Whether the engine could have survived the suggested routine became academic when Eldon Beagle pointed out that in terms of "operation," the criteria specified in the project document for the successful completion of Phase 1 only required

that the engine be demonstrated producing 5 hp while consuming less husk than would be produced while milling rice. There was no mention of how long it should operate, a bit of an oversight of ours in preparing the project proposal.

The furnace was fired up again, and this time the engine came through with flying colors. The engine easily demonstrated that it could produce more than 5 hp while consuming less than half of the husk produced during milling. I happily declared that the engine looked like it could be made in Bangladesh, and the demonstration was declared successfully completed. Graham Walker could now declare a "go" for Phase 2.

There were three additional issues. The engine was not yet a stand-alone unit as it depended on an external water supply for cooling, an electrically powered furnace blower, and a shop compressor to pressurize the air inside the engine. After considerable discussion we decided that the prototype should be shipped to Dhaka for testing with a rice huller and that work on integrating the auxiliaries would be done by us as we designed and fabricated the next generation of the engine in Bangladesh. Second, Sunpower requested that they be given two months to work with the engine before shipping it by air freight to Dhaka in October, so the start of Phase 2 was pushed back to the beginning of November 1982. Finally, it was recommended that we recruit an engineering graduate in Dhaka to assist me in the project.

Chapter 4
THE PROTOTYPE IN BANGLADESH

The prototype engine was shipped at the end of October, and Bruce Chagnot arrived in Dhaka on November 9 to set it up and get it running with a rice huller.

For months I had been working on adapting the engine design so that we could make it in Bangladesh. For many parts this involved going from welded assemblies to castings. For these I made drawings for the patternmaker, and the patterns were then delivered to one of the foundries we were using to produce castings. It so happened that early on the day that Bruce arrived I had picked up the casting for the crankcase of our first engine. I just had time to drop this at the end of the driveway at our house before heading to the airport to pick up Bruce. As I returned with Bruce and pulled into the drive, the crankcase casting was dead ahead of us. I was glowing with pride, as this represented the solution to a number of design problems, and after machining, would ensure the accurate alignment of the engine's fairly complicated linkage. As we drew to a stop Bruce stared at the casting. I waited for his exclamation of wonderment, but he was frowning when he said, "What's that?"

Figure 4.1

The engine foundation being prepared for the prototype engine.

The next day as we waited for the elevator to take us up to the USAID offices Bruce urged me not to make any changes in the design of the prototype and to concentrate on doing a quality job of fabricating it the same way Sunpower had. This put me firmly between a rock and a hard place, for I knew that trying to do things we were not good at, and not doing the things we were good at, would not only be frustrating but would certainly lead to a poorly made engine. Without any assurance from me that I would mend my ways, Bruce said that he would do what was required of him in terms of technical backup but that there wouldn't be any extra miles put in on his part.

The prototype was finally cleared from customs, and on November 29 it was uncrated at the project site (Fig. 4.1). By this time the engine shed was finished, complete with a rice huller installed and holes in the concrete floor for the prototype's foundation, plus an ash pit for the furnace.

Shortly before this time, as Sunpower had suggested earlier in August, we had hired a recent graduate from the Bangladesh University of Engineering and Technology in Dhaka to assist me in the project. Bruce was pleased that we had recruited a "real" engineer for the project, but it was not long before disillusionment set in. When Bruce quizzed him about the project engine, our engineer cheerily said that it must be a steam engine. Apparently he had never heard of Stirling engines. What was worse, he didn't seem very interested in what we were trying to accomplish. Bruce was totally mystified that there could be an engineering graduate who didn't share at least

Figure 4.2

Arranging insulating firebricks that have been cut for the furnace

part of his enthusiasm for these wonderful machines. With his suspicions aroused, Bruce gave our engineer a simple problem to solve: measure the volume of water in the large tank that would supply cooling water to our engine. In our arrangement the cooling water, after passing through the engine, would be returned to the tank so that during a run the temperature of the water in the tank would gradually increase. Given the number of kilowatts of heat that the engine was expected to reject into the cooling water, the question was, "How much would the temperature of the water in the tank increase after an engine run of eight hours?" After studying this problem for a while it was clear that our man didn't have a clue as to how to solve it.

The final straw came a few days later. Often, if an important person visited Mrs. Pati at the KWT Head Office, she would send them over to have a look at what we were doing with our Stirling engine. On this day, Bruce, standing in the ash pit, was plastering the furnace with muddied hands when the VIP was guided to the shed by one of the KWT office staff. Our engineer, attired in neatly ironed slacks and shirt, had been watching Bruce from a safe distance. As the VIP arrived he held out his immaculately clean hand to greet the visitor and introduced himself as "the concerned engineer." No one else in the project seemed to merit an introduction. If looks could kill, Bruce would have dropped "the concerned engineer" dead on the spot. To this saga there was a happy ending. Many, if not most, engineering graduates in Bangladesh aspire to the security of a government job, and when such a position was offered to our man he jumped at the opportunity. I like to think that his association with us helped him on his way. Certainly we were happy to see him move into a secure job with the government. The subject of hiring an engineer for the project was never raised again.

Figure 4.3

Bruce is checking the position of the partially completed furnace.

The Furnace

The cyclone husk furnace had worked well in Ohio except that its capacity was less than what was needed to run the engine steadily at full power. After he arrived in Dhaka, Bruce designed and made a somewhat larger furnace for the engine. Insulating firebricks were laid up to determine the outside dimensions (Fig. 4.2), and a sheet-metal drum made to fit. The bulk of the furnace lining was insulating fire brick, with only a half-inch coating of fire clay to protect the soft bricks from abrasion and hold things in place. In Figure 4.3 Bruce, standing in the ash pit, is checking the position of the partially completed furnace in respect to the prototype engine. With this minimal amount of thermal mass in the furnace it was eventually possible to go from cold to operating temperature with the hot end at 600 °C in ten to fifteen minutes. Some time later a USAID-funded project in the Philippines acquired a similar Stirling engine from Sunpower, for which a more robust furnace with regular firebricks was built. There was apparently some puzzlement when it took the better part of a working day and a huge amount of fuel to get up to operating temperature before the engine could even be started! Their problem was that the massive firebrick lining was absorbing most of the heat.

Figure 4.4

The completed furnace with its husk hopper and electric blower fitted to the prototype. Hoses supply cooling water; the compressor in the background will be used to pressurize the air in the engine.

First Bangladesh runs

The furnace, engine foundation, and husk feeding system were completed shortly before Christmas (Fig. 4.4). On December 24 the big moment came for the first run of the prototype in Bangladesh. Some burning coals from a fire were spooned into the furnace, and an electric blower supplied the combustion air, while a hand-operated augur fed rice husk from a hopper into the air stream just before it entered the furnace. The furnace worked well, and when the hot end temperature reached 600 °C the engine started easily. The excitement of the first run in Bangladesh was brief as the engine had to be shut down immediately due to some serious knocking sounds from inside. After opening the engine we found that a radiation baffle in the displacer had broken loose and a displacer con rod pin had slipped.

Fortunately, a replacement displacer had been shipped along with the engine, so early the next day (it was now Christmas) we returned to Narayanganj to fix the slipping pin on the displacer con rod and install the new displacer can. After the repairs were completed Bruce started the furnace with the electric blower as water from the tap flowed though the engine's cooler (Fig. 4.5). After ten minutes or so the temperature of the furnace and the engine's hot end was high enough to start the engine. Once the engine was running, our shop compressor was used to raise the pressure of the working air in the engine. As the pressure increased towards 4 bar the speed and power of the engine increased. After running the engine unloaded, it was stopped, de-pressurized, belted to the rice huller and restarted. With the furnace already hot, it took only a minute or two to re-pressurize the engine and

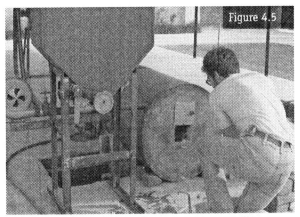

Figure 4.5

Starting the furnace; a hand crank operates an auger in the hopper to feed rice husk into the air stream as it enters the furnace.

get up to the power needed to mill rice. There was great excitement as, for the first time ever, rice milled using a husk-fueled Stirling engine flowed from the huller (Fig. 4.6). The next morning Bruce headed back to the USA.

I had assumed that we would be able to

Figure 4.6

Momotaz operates the No. 4 huller as rice is milled with a husk-fueled Stirling engine for the first time.

Figure 4.7

Monju records temperatures during a run. The tape recorder keeps track of the various noises emanating from the engine.

belt the prototype engine to the rice huller, tweak a few things, and start milling rice on a daily basis while work on our locally made engine progressed. There were several reasons why this was not to be.

First, the prototype engine was in no way a perfected design, and it turned out that solving design and fabrication problems would occupy most of our attention during the next four years before the project ended.

Second, there were problems controlling engine speed. The engine had no governor, which posed no problem when operating with a constant load such as the water pump. But a steel (Engleberg) rice huller is a different creature. Typically a milling run would start with

the huller unloaded and the engine running free. To start the milling, the inlet is opened till rice flows freely from the hopper through the machine. Next the flow of rice emerging from the outlet is gradually restricted with a sliding gate (or more often the operator's thumb) till the pressure inside builds up and the correct milling action is achieved (Fig. 3.9 and 4.6). If the rice flow into the huller becomes excessive or if the outlet is closed too much the huller will jam and stall, and the flat belt then slips off the pulley, allowing the engine to run unloaded. At this point the huller has to be opened and cleaned out before re-starting. This also entails stopping the engine to re-belt the huller before resum-

44

Figure 4.8

Checking the dismantled engine for wear

ing milling. For the Stirling engine, which had no governor, speed control was managed by having someone braking the engine when needed, by levering a piece of wood against the flywheel.

Temperatures of the hot end were monitored with four thermocouples fixed on the outside with ceramic cement. Two thermocouples were cemented to the dome, one in the center and one off-center. The third and fourth thermocouples were cemented to the fins. The prototype hot end did not have fittings that would enable us to monitor air temperatures inside the engine. Additional thermocouples measured cooling water inlet and outlet temperatures. Thermocouples were selected with a rotary switch, and read-

ings were taken using a digital temperature readout and recorded manually (Fig. 4.7).

Airflow to the cyclone burner was not varied. To maintain the heater temperature at about 600 °C the husk feed was increased or decreased, keeping an eye on the thermocouple readout.

Disassembly and inspection

On January 2 we disassembled the engine to check the condition of the mechanism and make needed repairs. The working parts of the engine could be extracted without dismounting the cooler and hot end (Fig. 4.8), but to fully disassemble the engine these were removed, revealing the inside of the furnace (Fig. 4.9). Figure 4.10 shows the hot end with

A view into the furnace after the first runs

The base of the hot end showing the regenerator, which is made of 4 kg of knitted 0.004″ stainless steel wire. A sample of the regenerator material is in front.

its regenerator and a sample of the Metex knitted stainless-steel wire regenerator in the foreground. The engine used 4 kg of regenerator material tightly packed in the annular space at the base of the hot end.

Figure 4.11 shows the aluminum cooler with the steel cylinder liner and wrap-around sheet stainless-steel cooling water jacket. The moving parts of the prototype, except the crankshaft, are seen in Figure 4.12, with a closer view of the piston and its linkage in Figure 4.13. The design of the prototype had originally called for a greased leather cup seal for the piston. This had created too much drag, and it was replaced by a PTFE tube fitted in the large ring groove in the piston. There are two connecting rods operating from the crank throw (Fig. 4.14). The main connecting rod drives the piston through two piston links, and this articulated linkage is supported by a swing link that minimized side forces on the piston. The smaller displacer connecting rod drives

the bell crank, which in turn is connected to the displacer rod by a short link. This provides the necessary phase difference—the displacer "top dead center" occurs 69.6 degrees before piston "top dead center." The crankshaft and bearing assembly are shown in Figure 4.15 and consist of an inner needle bearing, an outer ball bearing, and a machined Rulon (filled PTFE) pressure seal. The main connecting-rod bearing is fitted to the outside of the crank throw (Fig. 4.16); the bell crank connecting rod is fitted with a hardened pin that rides in the smaller needle bearing on the inside of the throw. Figure 4.17 shows the main connecting rod with its needle bearing, wrist pins for the piston links, and the swing link.

Figure 4.11

A view of the prototype cooler showing the cylinder and its internal porting

The piston, displacer, and linkage

A close view showing the articulated connection between the piston links and the main con rod, which is supported by the swing link. The displacer rod passes through the piston and is attached to the bell crank with a short link.

Figure 4.14

The main con rod and displacer con rod both connect to the crank throw, which is not shown here.

Figure 4.15

The crankshaft runs in an inner needle bearing and an outer ball bearing. The pressure seal is machined from a Rulon/PTFE alloy.

A close view of the crank throw. The main con rod rides on the outer bearing sleeve while a pin on the displacer con rod rides on the inner needle bearing.

The main con rod and swing link. The steel rod had been brazed in place to strengthen the steel casting

After the Christmas and New Year break, we made arrangements for a demonstration run for USAID. I was pretty sure that the linkage would not survive long at full power, so the run was kept to a few minutes. Figure 4.18 shows the group of USAID and Asia Foundation people gathered at the project site in January 1983. As an aside it is interesting to note, in the foreground, one of many Ipil ipil (*Leucaena leucocephala*) seedlings planted at the site that

Figure 4.18

Getting ready for the demonstration run of the prototype for a group from USAID in January 1983

Figure 4.19

Spooning live coals into the furnace

Figure 4.20

Collecting coals from a fire to start the furnace

the same tree after only seventeen months of growth.

To start the furnace, some burning waste or live coals from a fire were spooned into the central port at the rear of the furnace (Fig. 4.19, 4.20). The port was then closed and the electric blower started while slowly turning the husk feed by hand. In a little more than ten minutes the furnace and hot end were hot enough to start the engine. At this time the furnace blower, the compressor to pressurize the crankcase to about 4 bar, and the cooling water were all externally supplied. Once the engine was running, we milled some rice for the onlookers (Fig. 4.21), and a few minutes later things were shut down without any mechanical mishaps. While the demonstration run was short, it was also sweet, and everyone was happy to see the rice husk–fueled prototype Stirling engine operating in Bangladesh.

Prototype postmortem

After the demonstration, the prototype was again disassembled and examined. During the short demonstration run the bell crank had developed a crack (Fig. 4.22). It was fortunate that the run had not been longer than a few minutes or we would certainly have had an embarrassing breakdown. It was clear by this time that the prototype engine was beyond repairing and we would not be able to use it to operate the rice mill, so it was

eventually showed the amazing growth potential of this tree in the warm, wet, and fertile conditions of Bangladesh. Figure 9.20 shows

51

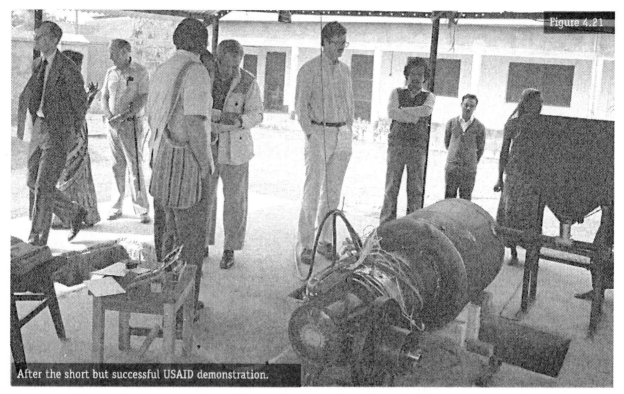

After the short but successful USAID demonstration.

Figure 4.21

slated for mothballs and a list of problems to be dealt with in our next engine was drawn up:

- A new, stronger bell crank design was needed.
- The Xylan coating on the displacer rod (Fig. 4.23), the piston and the displacer (Fig. 4.24) were badly abraded after less than an hour or two of running, so an alternative system to avoid wear was needed.
- The needle bearings in the displacer drive were too small.
- The end of the displacer rod needed to be supported to prevent it from pressing on the piston and increasing piston ring drag.
- The mechanism was noisy, indicating loose tolerances.
- A better piston ring was needed.

- The steel cylinder, which was a shrink fit in the aluminum cooler, had become oval shaped, allowing air to leak past the piston.
- Gasket material was used for the seal between the crank case and cooler, and between the cooler and the hot end. This was prone to leak after being disassembled and re-assembled a few times. A temporary solution was to use silicone sealant as a gasket seal.
- Silicone sealant was also used to seal the cooler jacket to the cooler; this would not be suitable for rural Bangladesh.
- The blower for the furnace, air compressor, and coolant pump still needed to be integrated with the engine design.

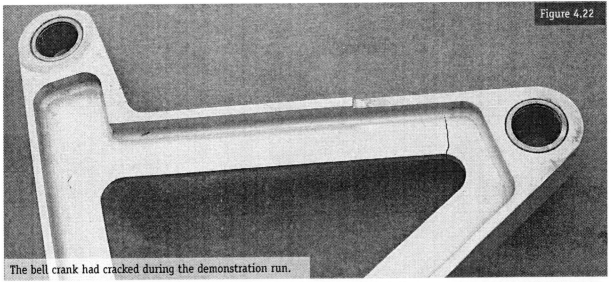

Figure 4.22

The bell crank had cracked during the demonstration run.

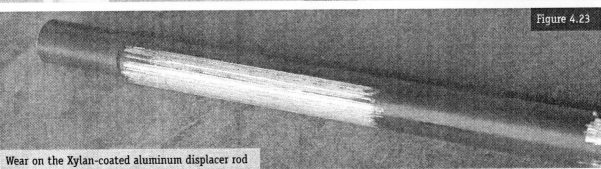

Figure 4.23

Wear on the Xylan-coated aluminum displacer rod

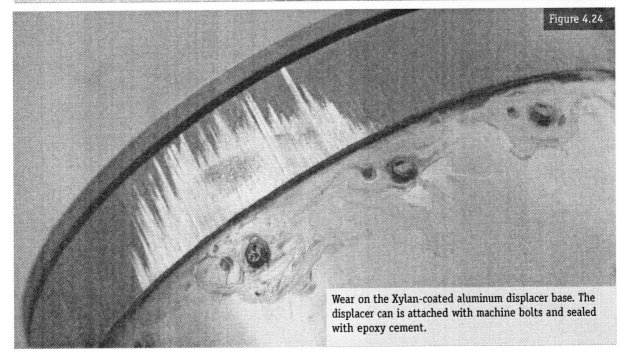

Figure 4.24

Wear on the Xylan-coated aluminum displacer base. The displacer can is attached with machine bolts and sealed with epoxy cement.

Chapter 5

DESIGN OF THE FIRST INTERMEDIATE MODEL

(IM-1)

Long before the prototype was finished and running in Ohio, I had begun to design parts for our first intermediate model. Many of these involved design changes that would make the best use of the different resources available in Bangladesh as compared with the USA. In some cases we were more limited in what we could do; in other cases we could get work done cheaply and easily that would be beyond consideration cost-wise in the USA for one-off components. While some of the design changes were made to facilitate fabrication, many others were made to deal with the problems that had emerged during the operation of the prototype engine.

The most significant design change in production methods was the switch from a welded mild steel assembly for the crankcase to a cast-iron crankcase and separate cast-iron bearing case. Good welding skills were hard to come by in Bangladesh even for single jobs, and the prospects of maintaining high standards of welding in serial production would be slim. On the other hand, cast iron is a familiar medium with the skilled pattern-makers, foundry men, and machinists available, and they could reliably maintain the tolerances required for the RHEP engine.

Crankcase

To facilitate casting, machining, and assembly, the new crankcase design incorporated a separate bearing case on one side and on the opposite side an inspection port. This arrangement facilitated assembly and disassembly, and enabled us to observe the linkage in operation after the engine was assembled.

Main con rod

The main connecting rod of the prototype was machined from a steel casting. After the breakdown during the August demonstration in Ohio, the steel casting had been strengthened with a welded crossbar. As steel castings were not an option for us in Bangladesh, the main con rod was redesigned with more metal, including a cross web, and made of cast iron.

Cooler

The prototype cooler was machined from a large casting that also formed the middle structural element of the engine. Because of the difficulty in getting large aluminum castings that had no porous spots, the aluminum cooler was reduced to the minimum possible size and enclosed in a cast-iron body. The cast-iron body provided the structural element joining the crankcase to the hot end and also served as the outside jacket for the cooling water. Even with the smaller aluminum casting, we still had small porous spots and leaks, though these could be patched up. Our cooler problem was only eliminated when a completely new cooler design was adopted in the project's last engine.

Design changes to solve problems

Some of the original design features of the prototype had proven to be inadequate and were addressed in the design of the first intermediate model.

Wearing surfaces

The wearing surfaces of the piston, displacer, and displacer rod were anodized aluminum coated with Xylan (similar to the surfaces of Teflon-coated frying pans). While this had been relatively successful in Sunpower's hermetically sealed free-piston engines, in the less-than-pristine environment inside our prototype, floating particles eventually abraded the Xylan layer, and degradation increased rapidly thereafter, as can be seen in Figures 4.23 and 4.24.

Piston rings

Originally the piston was to be sealed with a greased leather cup seal. This had generated too much drag and was replaced with a PTFE tube fitted in the same groove with butted ends. While this sufficed for the demonstration runs, it was far from optimal in terms of sealing and for guidance for the piston. In the new design a longer piston skirt had two Teflon wear rings that also served as compression rings. Initially these rings were 10 mm wide and cut from 1/8 inch–thick virgin PTFE sheet.

Cylinder liner

The thin steel cylinder liner of the prototype was heat-shrunk into the cooler and then bored to size. After some time the cylinder liner had become oval, and this resulted in significant leakage of air past the rings. The IM-1 cylinder was machined from a cast-iron sleeve with a finished thickness of 5 mm and was a sliding fit inside the cooler.

Sealing

The working space in the engine was pressurized to as much as 5 bar (70 psi), so the external joints and crankshaft had to be sealed. In the prototype, when bolting the hot end to the cooler and the cooler to the crankcase, the mating faces were smeared with silicone sealant to make them leak-proof. In the IM-1 these joints were machined with grooves and sealed with O-rings. This facilitated rapid disassembly and re-assembly, and the O-rings could be repeatedly reused. The workers became so adept at this that they could strip the engine down in ten to fifteen minutes. As they say, practice makes perfect.

The crankshaft of the prototype used a pressure seal machined from Rulon (filled PTFE). In the IM-1 we had leather cup seals made for us locally, which were greased.

We found that these had to be replaced after a few disassembly/assembly cycles, and later we switched to a standard automotive spring-activated oil seal.

Displacer rod and spider

In the prototype, the displacer rod passed through the piston and was connected to the bell crank by means of a short link. This link made it possible for the bell crank arm that moves in an arc to drive the displacer rod, which moves in a straight line. There was still a small up-and-down force on the rod that acted on the piston, resulting in considerable wear at the top and bottom of the piston skirt. This problem was resolved in our engines by supporting the displacer rod at the base of the cylinder by means of a spider in which a PTFE bush guided the displacer rod. The short link was eliminated by having a flexible drive rod inside the displacer tube. The single bearing at the end of the flexible link could follow the arc of the bell crank arm while exerting only a slight side force.

Displacer linkage

Perhaps the biggest problem we encountered was inadequate strength in the engine's linkage, particularly that of the displacer. This problem was related to the fact that the engine had no governor. The displacer linkage had been designed for a lighter load than the piston, since it takes relatively little power to shuttle the air inside the engine back and forth compared to the power being transmitted from the piston out of the engine through the crankshaft. However, a serious problem arose if the engine was run unloaded. If the belt to a rice huller slipped off and the engine ran free, the displacer, pushing 7 liters of air back and forth inside the engine, acted as a brake. The speed would increase till the braking effect of the displacer balanced the power from the piston. Soon the displacer linkage would be transmitting the maximum power of the engine. In the course of the project we made numerous modifications to strengthen the displacer linkage, but ultimately none were fully successful. Only when a new engine design was developed with a different linkage system was the problem solved.

Unresolved design features

For the first intermediate model, we focused attention on making most of the engine, while some tasks were put off till later. We used the prototype hot end that incorporated the regenerator, so fabricating this most challenging component was tackled later. The furnace blower, compressor, and water cooling pump were yet to be integrated with the engine. Finally, we needed to instrument the engine so we could monitor operating parameters and make accurate power measurements.

Chapter 6
MAKING THE FIRST INTERMEDIATE MODEL

The original plan for the Rice Husk Energy Project workshop was to have a modest range of tools and equipment for fitting and assembly and to rely on the main Kumudini Welfare Trust workshop to carry out most of the machining operations. We reasoned that this work would be done in the periods that the main workshop was not preoccupied repairing a broken-down jute press or overhauling a tugboat. Not long after the project started we could see that this arrangement would not be practical and decided to fully equip the RHEP workshop. A large Indian lathe and later a

medium-sized Chinese all-geared lathe were procured. Kumudini shifted a large radial-arm drill from their dock and a universal milling machine from the central workshop to our project. Both of these British-made machine tools turned out to be invaluable for our work, and it was very convenient to have them close at hand.

In re-designing the engine we capitalized on the availability of skilled patternmakers (Fig. 6.1) and several different foundries. Most of the iron casting was done in a small foundry, (Fig. 6.2) where melts were done in a crucible heated

Pattern makers working on the pattern for the unsuccessful first design for the engine body

In a small foundry, molten cast iron is poured into a series of moulds. The crucible has been heated in a small gas-fired furnace.

59

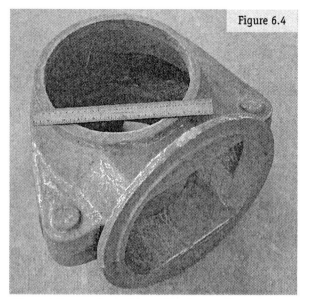

The cast iron crankcase for our first intermediate model

After turning its flange on a lathe, the crankcase was mounted on the milling machine, where it remained un-moved for most of the remaining machining operations. Here the near side is being faced.

by natural gas with an electric blower supplying the combustion air. Several melts were done each day, so if a pattern was given in the morning we could usually pick up the casting in the afternoon. Sometimes the casting was not long out of the mould when we picked it up, and was still too hot to handle. The problem was easily solved with a loop of heavy twine that formed a carrying handle. The charge for iron castings was about one dollar a kilogram. Large iron

castings like the crankcase and body were done in a large foundry with a cupola furnace that was fired once every week or two. Non-ferrous castings were done in another small foundry that specialized in aluminum and gun metal (bronze) casting.

From Phase 2 onwards there were half-yearly reviews held in Bangladesh, usually in May and November. In Fig. 6.3 the May 1983 review team was meeting in Mrs. Pati's office at Kumudini Welfare Trust with rep-

The project review team in May 1983: from left to right, Mary Fontaine (TAF), Craig Kinzelman (Sunpower), Bob Barnes (USAID), Eldon Beagle (TAF), Bruce Chagnot (Sunpower), Mrs. Joya Pati (KWT), Mr. Callahan (USAID), Sherry Plunkett (USAID).

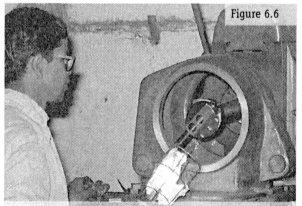

Fly-cutting the face of the far side of the crankcase with the boring head mounted on a long arbor

Figure 6.7

After the crankcase was bored to size, the seats for the bell crank and swing link pivots were drilled and reamed. Here the pivot seats are being faced.

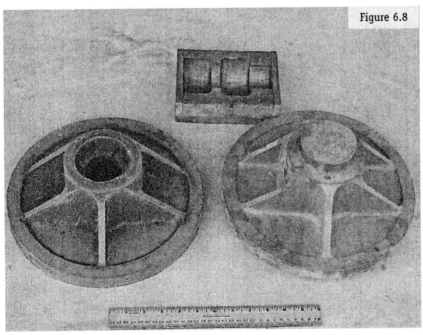
Figure 6.8

The pattern (right), core box (top), and casting (left) for the bearing case

resentatives from the Asia Foundation, Sunpower, and USAID.

Crankcase

The design of the crankcase incorporated two large symmetrical side ports that accommodated the bearing case on one side and an inspection port on the opposite side (Fig. 6.4). Machining the flange that bolted to the body proved to be a problem as there was no easy way to hold the casting in a lathe. This was solved by casting and machining two angle plates that enabled us to mount the crankcase on the faceplate of the large lathe. The remaining operations were carried out on the milling machine, which was still in the KWT workshop at this point. Figure 6.5 shows the near side of the casting being fly cut. Using a long arbor, the far side of the crankcase was similarly faced and then bored to size (Fig. 6.6). Without moving the casting, the holes for the swing link and bell crank pivots were drilled, reamed, and then faced with a fly cutter (Fig. 6.7). By completing this machining sequence in

The abortive first design for the engine body mounted on the planning machine to have the feet faced

The foundation for the second version of the engine body nearing completion

one setting on the milling machine we could be sure that the pivots and crankshaft would be accurately aligned and perpendicular to the axis of the cylinder.

Bearing case

Having the bearing case and crankcase as separate castings simplified the design and machining operations. But, as with other castings, this added to the weight of the engine. Figure 6.8 shows the bearing case casting, core box, and pattern. The crankshaft of the IM-1 engine was mounted in the bearing case with standard deep-groove ball-bearing races. The pressure seal was a custom-made leather cup seal packed with grease.

Body

In some of my early designs for castings I made the mistake of trying to integrate several features in one casting. This was easy to do on the drawing board, problematic for the patternmaker, difficult to cast, and sometimes impossible to machine. So it was with my first

body design that I happily incorporated cast feet. This involved complicated pattern-making and resulted in a huge casting. Figure 6.9 shows the feet of this casting being faced on an old but wonderful metal-planing machine driven through a flat belt from an overhead line shaft in the Kumudini workshop. In the end there was no way to mount the casting on our milling machine, and the design was scrapped. The second version of the body omitted the feet and could easily be machined. In the first intermediate model the body was anchored to the foundation with the hot end bolted to one end and the crankcase to the other end (Fig. 6.10).

Finned aluminum cooler

One of the most problematic components of the engine was its cooler. In the prototype the aluminum cooler also formed the structural connection between the hot end and the crankcase, so the casting was large. In our engines a cast-iron body physically connected the hot end and crankcase and also formed

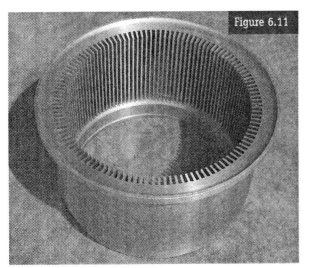

After we machined the aluminum cooler sleeve on one of our lathes, it was taken to a specialty shop, where the internal fins were cut on a vertical slotting machine.

Filing the leading edges of the internal fins to reduce air flow friction. At this time we didn't realize that the spots on the casting by Fazul's knee represented a porous spot and would pose a serious problem for us.

the outer jacket of the cooler. This greatly reduced the size of the aluminum cooler casting. After machining the cooler on a lathe, we took it to an industrial assistance organization equipped with a large vertical slotting machine to have the internal slots cut (Fig. 6.11). The leading edges of the internal fins were filed to provide streamlining, (Fig. 6.12) and finally the external grooves for cooling

water were milled (Fig. 6.13).

As an alternative for the aluminum cooler I designed one that would make use of copper tubes. The body of this first model, the copper tube cooler, was a large iron casting that also served as the body and the cylinder of the engine. It was drilled to receive a large num-

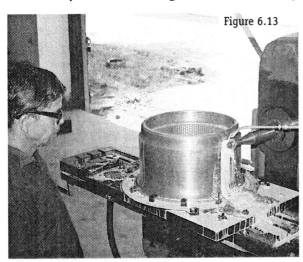

Figure 6.13

Radha milling the external cooling-water grooves on the aluminum cooler

Figure 6.14

Fitting the aluminum cooler and cast iron cylinder in the engine body. The castings for the first copper tube cooler are in front of the packing crate.

Drilling holes for the copper tubes in the cast iron cooler body

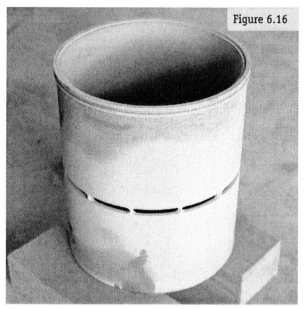

The cast iron cylinder with milled ports

ber of copper tubes through which air would move from the hot end to the cold end of the engine. Cooling water would be confined by a cast-iron jacket. The castings for the cooler body and the water jacket can be seen in front of the empty packing crate in Figure 6.14. In this picture Fazul has fitted the aluminum cooler and cylinder in the body of the engine. A second crankcase, in front of the work table, is about to be mounted on a lathe faceplate with two cast-iron angle plates. In Figure 6.15 Momotaz is drilling holes for the copper tubes in the cast-iron cooler body. The problem we ran into was that because of the mass of the cooler casting, we couldn't achieve the necessary temperatures for brazing the copper tubes to the body, and this design was abandoned.

Cylinder liner

The thin steel cylinder of the prototype had become oval to the point that there was significant leakage past the piston ring. We made our cylinder from cast iron as a sliding

fit in the cooler with a wall thickness of 5 mm. The Xylan that was never used as an antifriction coating for the piston and displacer was put to good use as an anti-corrosive coating for the outside of the cylinder (Fig. 6.16).

Crankshaft assembly

The crankshaft was built up from a mild steel shaft with a cast-iron counterweight/web. In Figure 6.17 a key-way is being milled for the crankshaft to flywheel key. Figure 6.18

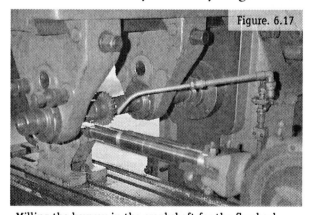

Milling the keyway in the crankshaft for the flywheel

Figure 6.18

Our first crankshaft (right) and a later model with more counterweight. The crank throw is about to be fitted in the new crankshaft assembly (left).

shows two crankshafts with different sizes of counterweights. The throw of one has yet to be installed. This is done by drilling and fixing with a spring pin (Fig. 6.19). In Figure 6.20 the crankshaft has been assembled with the bearing case, and the cast-iron bell crank connecting rod is in place.

Piston linkage

Figure 6.20

The crank throw is fixed in place by drilling and fitting a spring pin.

Figure 6.19

The finished crankshaft assembly fitted in the bearing case. The inner sleeve of the main con rod bearing and the displacer con rod have been fitted.

Figure 6.21

The main con rod casting (left) with its pattern and core box.

Figure 6.22

The main con rod mounted on a purpose-made angle plate being marked out for machining

Figure 6.23

After it has been marked out, the main con rod casting, still on the angle plate, is mounted on the milling machine for boring and facing.

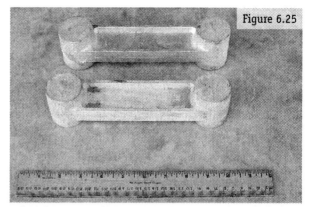

Figure 6.25

The pattern and aluminum casting used to make the piston links

Figure 6.26

Boring the piston link for bronze bushings

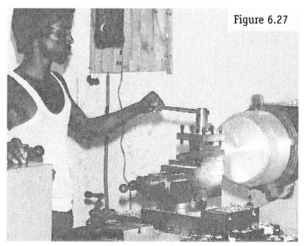

Figure 6.27

Turning the crown of the Model-A piston casting

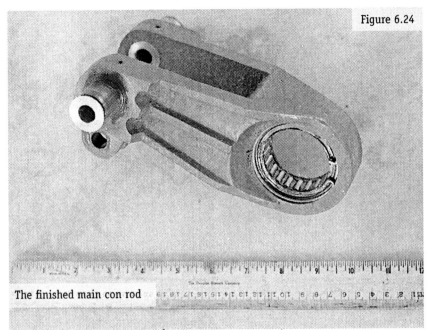

Figure 6.24

The finished main con rod

In the prototype the main connecting rod was made from a steel casting. As this option was not available in Bangladesh the design was made heavier with an integral web and cast in iron. Figure 6.21 shows the finished casting, pattern, and core box for the main connecting rod. The main connecting rod casting was mounted on an angle plate and the positions for pins and bearings marked out (Fig. 6.22, 6.23). The con rod remained on the jig for the boring operations. The completed main connecting rod with bearing and pins installed is shown in Figure 6.24.

Our first piston links were cast in aluminum (Fig. 6.25). After facing on the lathe they were bored to be fitted with oil-impregnated sintered bronze bushes (Fig. 6.26).

Piston

The initial piston design made use of a single aluminum casting similar to that of the prototype but with a longer skirt and two piston rings. Having two rings eliminated a problem with the piston tilting in the cylinder. The crown was cast with extra material for the lathe chuck to grip; in Figure 6.27 this sacrificial material is being turned to provide a grip for the lathe chuck. Figure 6.28 shows the piston itself being turned. Drilling and reaming the piston to receive the piston pins was possible, but it was difficult to maintain accurate alignment. A later two-part design for the piston simplified this operation.

Displacer linkage

The displacer is driven through a bell crank so that its movement is out of phase with the movement of the piston. In the IM-1 and the IM-2 engines, as with the prototype, the displacer top dead center occurs about 69 degrees before piston top dead center. One arm of the bell crank is connected to the main crankshaft throw by the displacer con rod. The other arm of the bell crank drives the displacer by means of a flexible displacer rod (Fig. 8.20), which is fitted inside the displacer tube. Using a flexible link eliminated the need for the separate link used in the prototype to connect the

Figure 6.28

Turning the skirt of the one-piece piston

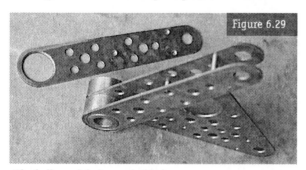

Figure 6.29

The bell crank being assembled

Figure 6.30

Boring the seats for the bell crank bearing pins

bell crank to the displacer rod.

By this time it was clear that an aluminum bell crank would not be strong enough. The prototype bell crank machined from tough alloy stock had cracked, and by comparison locally cast aluminum material would have considerably less strength. As an alternative, a bell crank was designed that was built up from mild steel plate by welding and riveting (Fig. 6.29). In Figure 6.30 the seats for the bearing pins are being bored on the lathe. In this design the arms of the bell crank were offset, a feature that eventually proved to be a problem.

In the prototype the displacer rod was not supported at its end, and this had led to some misalignment and drag. To avoid this problem in our engine I designed a spider that was fitted at the base of the cylinder. The spider was fitted with a PTFE bush through which the displacer tube slid back and forth, thus maintaining accurate alignment. The prototype's displacer rod was connected to the bell crank with a short link. This was replaced by a tube with a long flexible link inside that could be connected directly to the arm of the bell crank.

Displacer

The displacer can of the Sunpower prototype was made by forming 0.7 mm stainless-steel sheet into a cylinder and TIG-welding the seam. The dome was made by clamping a stainless-steel blank to a heavy steel plate with a steel ring sealed with O-rings. Hydraulic fluid pumped into the space between the base plate and blank caused it to bulge. This bulged dome was trimmed and TIG-welded to a stainless steel ring, which in turn was welded to the displacer can. Radiation baffles were formed from stainless steel sheet that was cut and spot welded to form a shallow cone. Tabs along the edge of these cones allowed several of them to be spot welded inside the displacer can along its length. These effectively blocked radiation but did not provide much support for the walls of the displacer. The finished displacer can was attached to the aluminum displacer body with small machine screws and sealed with epoxy.

Explosive forming (part 1)

Having read a bit about explosive forming, I decided to give this approach a try. For one thing, it promised to be a lot more exciting than hydraulically bulging a dome, rather like reliving childhood adventures. Early work on explosive forming had made use of shotgun shells with the shot removed, so my first stop was at a gun shop in Dhaka. It soon became apparent that there was no way that I could get shotgun shells as I was not a licensed gun owner. As this was being explained to me my eyes fell on a big glass jar on the counter filled with about 4 liters of gunpowder and pellets. The shopkeeper explained to me that after repairing the firing mechanism of a shotgun they would put a shell, emptied of powder and shot, in the gun and fire it to see if the cap went off properly.

"Can I get some of this surplus powder?" I asked.

"Please come back tomorrow."

The next day when I returned, I got a firm negative. I suppose my explanation of what I wanted the powder for was so farfetched as to arouse all sorts of suspicions.

My next stop was at a small shop selling fireworks in Narayanganj, not far from our workshop. Here I hit pay dirt, for Tk5, Tk10 and Tk15 each (US$0.18-$0.50) I could get firecrackers that were more like little bombs. They were made by winding jute string around a paper packet of powder with a small bamboo tube leading the fuse out. Popular sizes ranged from that of a hard ball up to soft-ball size. Even the smallest would blow an empty gallon paint can to shreds. Since explosive forming is done with the die immersed in water, I removed the bamboo fuses and replaced them with lamp-cord wire leading to a short length of a single strand of copper wire (from the lamp cord) as a fuse. The firecracker was then repeatedly dipped in wax to render it quite waterproof.

A big advantage of explosive forming is that only a female die is required, so there is no need for accurate machining of male and female dies to match each other. Another advantage is that cast iron is quite satisfactory as a material for the dies. After machining the outer dimensions of the die, the trick was to cut the inside curve. A hole of one inch or more was drilled at the center of the die to nearly the final depth. The first cylindrical portion of the die was machined, and then I used a Lotus 1-2-3 spreadsheet that did a simple geometric calculation for the two curves (radius of the shoulder and

The die used in explosive forming of the displacer dome. The stainless steel blank will be clamped to the die with an O-ring seal to make it airtight.

radius of the dome) which gave how many divisions less on the cross feed to cut for each division on the longitudinal feed. A somewhat tedious process, but one that yielded good results. And with a bit of emery paper the fine ridges resulting from this technique were soon removed, leaving a reasonably smooth surface. To complete the die I turned an O-ring groove, and it was drilled and tapped for a vacuum fitting. Figure 6.31 shows the completed die before the clamping ring and blank have been fitted. The O-ring seal and the vacuum fitting allow the air to be removed before the metal is formed. A mild-steel flat bar handle facilitates moving and positioning the heavy die. In Figure 6.32 the clamping ring and blank have been fixed in position and the vacuum pump (a small refrigerator compressor and vacuum gauge) connected

to the die by a long copper tube.

In the first trials the die was placed in one of the parboiling drums (half an oil drum) filled with water (Fig. 6.33). The explosive had been suspended at about the center of the radius of the dome. After running the refrigerator compressor till the gauge showed a half-decent vacuum the two leads from the wire fuse in the explosive were touched (at a safe distance) to the terminals of a 12-volt car battery. The explosion was most satisfying (Fig. 6.34), but the blank was not fully formed (Fig. 6.35). It was a good start though.

To provide more water pressure, a full oil drum was half buried in the ground, and we stepped up one size in the firecracker range. In Figure 6.36 the die, blank, and attached explosive are ready to be placed in the tank. The explosion (Fig. 6.37) was bigger and the resulting dome (Fig. 6.38) almost fully

A refrigerator compressor is used to evacuate the space inside the die.

In the first test, the die was immersed in a half drum of water.

The charge is detonated

This stainless steel blank was not fully formed.

Ready for another test using a full drum of water, which is half buried in the ground. The explosive is positioned above the blank.

A bigger explosion

A fully formed dome. With more experience we eliminated most of the creases and irregularities seen here.

After parting on the lathe, this dome is ready to use as a baffle in the displacer.

formed with vertical edges suited for the spot welding to come. With deeper tanks we were later able to fully form the displacer domes and baffles without creases. In Figure 6.39 the displacer dome has been parted from the formed piece and is ready to assemble with the rest of the displacer can.

Spot welding the displacer

In the prototype Sunpwer had made extensive use of Tungsten Inert Gas (TIG) welding, which is well suited for stainless-steel, particularly thin sheet. At this time in Bangladesh it was not possible to get the argon gas needed for TIG welding. For the thicker (3 mm) stainless steel in the heater

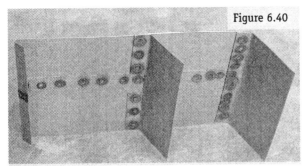

Figure 6.40

This test sample demonstrated the proposed method of using spot welding to make the displacer.

we were able to use conventional arc welding with flux-covered stainless steel electrodes. The displacer, however, was made from 0.7 mm stainless steel sheet, and this was too thin to be arc welded. After some experimenting (Figure 6.40) we decided to use closely spaced spot welds to assemble the displacer. The first attempts at spot welding the seam of the dis-

Figure 6.41

Part of the welding jig for making displacers. A groove is being cut in the casting where the lower electrode of the spot welder will be positioned.

placer produced a warped cylinder that was not improved when we tried to slide in the baffles. To solve this problem a fairly elaborate jig was developed. The jig consisted of a cast-iron sleeve with a longitudinal thickening inside. After machining the outer dimensions on a lathe the sleeve was mounted on the antique metal plane (Fig. 6.41) and grooved to accept the lower electrode of the spot welder. The completed jig consisted of the cast-iron sleeve mounted in a mild steel frame that also supported and guided the spot welder, allowing the electrodes to be positioned anywhere along the seam.

There were several advantages from using this jig. The sheet for the displacer can was first rolled and then tied onto the jig, which ensured that it remained accurately cylindrical. The seam was welded by randomly positioning weld spots, leaving plenty of time for the can to cool and slowly filling the entire seam with weld spots (Fig. 6.42). A packing strip between the can and the jig provided clearance so that, when it was removed, the can was a close but sliding fit on the jig and could easily be removed.

The jig also allowed the dome of the displacer to be accurately positioned and then spot welded in place (Fig. 6.43). Finally the baffles were positioned one at a time and fixed in place with a quite a few weld spots to provide good support for the displacer can. Figure 6.44 shows our first displacer can, which was attached to the cast-iron base with spot welds. Later we used small machine screws sealed with epoxy.

Hot end

The seam of the displacer can being spot-welded

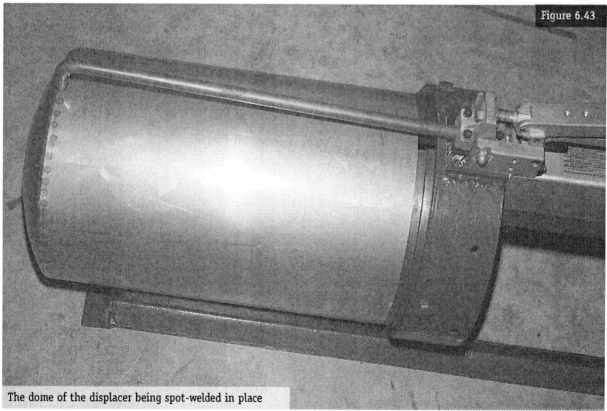

The dome of the displacer being spot-welded in place

Figure 6.44

The finished displacer

The first intermediate model was operated with the hot end from the prototype. During this period we explored a number of avenues in respect to making both the hot end and the material for the regenerator.

Searching for big presses, I discovered the Dhaka Drum Factory next to the old airport not far from the center of Dhaka. In contrast with the rest of Dhaka, which was becoming increasingly congested, the Drum Factory was surrounded by 10 acres of grass and trees. The factory was equipped with large American-made presses, power shears, and equipment to seam-weld the drums. It turned out that the facility had been set up during World War II, when Dhaka was a staging point for flights over the hump into Burma. I was impressed that all the equipment was still working smoothly. Although I never made use of their presses I regularly had them shear the 3-mm stainless sheet that we worked with.

Chapter 7

FIRST INTERMEDIATE MODEL OPERATION

(November 1983)

Work on the first intermediate model had progressed well, and some weeks before Bruce and Craig were due to arrive for the November 1983 review we assembled the engine and got ready for the first trial run. Many of the problems identified in the prototype had been solved in the process of designing and making our first intermediate model, and I was optimistic that the first run would go well.

We slid the furnace into position, placed a few scoops of burning charcoal inside, and turned on the electric blower. In the blast of air the charcoal glowed brightly and crackled with sparks. As rice husk was fed from the hopper into the air stream we could watch through the inspection port as the particles burst into flame. Soon the inside of the furnace was incandescent, and the temperature of the hot end climbed toward 600 °C. It was time to start the engine!

A few turns with the crank should have got it started but didn't. More cranking, still nothing, not even a hint that it wanted to run. Disappointed, we removed the furnace and opened the inspection port of the crankcase. My heart sank as I peered inside to find that water was leaking into the crankcase, making the engine inoperable.

Cooler crisis

We soon confirmed that water was leaking through the cooler. The rough spot I had noticed earlier was actually porous. The solution seemed pretty simple: we removed the cooler, cleaned up the porous area, and coated it with epoxy. After assembling the engine we ran water through the cooler and found to our dismay that it still leaked. Several repeats of this approach reduced but could not eliminate the pesky leak.

The irony with the aluminum cooler is that we pay a lot of money to make a large casting that is inclined to become porous, and then we pay more money to have most of this metal machined away. It doesn't make too much sense. On the other hand, copper tubing is available at low cost, and the walls are thin and more conductive to heat than aluminum.

Earlier I had attempted to make a cooler that incorporated copper tubes with a rather large cast-iron cylinder (Fig. 6.15). The problem came when I tried to braze the copper tubes in position on the cast-iron sleeve. I had successfully brazed copper tubes to a sample piece of cast iron, but the mass of cast iron in this first design sucked up heat from the torch

77

Turning the cast-iron sleeve for our second attempt at a cooler with copper tubes. The cooler also serves as the cylinder for the displacer.

Fitting copper tubes to the drilled cooler casting.

The cooler assembly with insulating firebricks inside, and ceramic wool on the outside to reduce heat loss while brazing

The cooler with all the copper tubes fitted

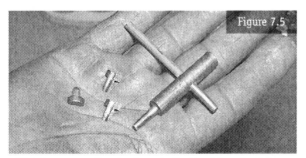

Miniature expanding tools made for the ¼″ cooler tubes.

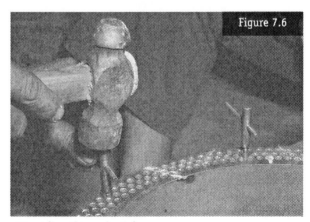

Expanding the cooler tubes

and made it impossible to achieve the necessary brazing temperature. At that time I had abandoned the idea of a copper tube cooler, but when we encountered the persistent problem of water leaking through our aluminum cooler, it was back to the drawing board for a tubular cooler with a much lighter and thinner cast-iron body (Fig. 7.1). After the cast-iron sleeve had been turned and drilled, I fitted the copper tubes (Fig. 7.2). The assembly was then filled with insulating firebricks and wrapped with ceramic wool to reduce heat loss (Figs. 7.3 and 7.4). In the next attempt at brazing we got closer but it was still not possible to get a good joint between the copper tubes and the cast-iron flanges.

Next I consulted texts on steam boiler maintenance and decided to try expanding the copper tubes in place. We made tiny expanding tools (Fig. 7.5) and set about expanding both ends of all the tubes (Fig. 7.6). Still we could not get a water-tight seal. Time was running out, and the last effort was to flow epoxy mixed with powdered graphite filler in the space between the tubes on the inside of the cooler where they joined the cast-iron flanges. Though this had promise, we still had some leaks.

By now our time was up, and in spite of working all night our coolers were still leaky. Feeling quite depressed, I drove back to Dhaka to get cleaned up and then go out to the airport to meet Bruce and Craig. I dreaded having to break the bad news. The plane was on time, and there were cheery greetings all around as the two emerged from immigration and customs.

Figure 7.7

The disassembled IM-1 engine

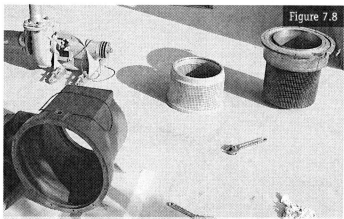

Figure 7.8

The IM-1 body on its foundation with the cooler and hot end

Figure 7.9

The IM-1 body with the cooler and cylinder liner installed

you do is pressurize the engine before starting the flow of cooling water. That way some air leaks out but water can't get in the engine." The relief I felt was like waking up from a nightmare to a sunny morning and welcoming world.

After lunch in Dhaka we drove the fifteen miles to the project site in Narayanganj and within an hour, following Bruce's suggested routine, our engine ran for the first time at 10:19 the morning of November 21, 1983—a very happy moment for all of us.

IM-1 assembly

Figure 7.7 shows the first intermediate model with all of its parts disassembled. The body of the engine was bolted to the foundation and did not have to be removed in order to disassemble the rest of the engine (Fig. 7.8). In Figure 7.9 the cooler and cylinder liner have been installed in the body. In Figure 7.10 the hot end is being attached, after which the displacer, piston, and spider assembly are slid into place (Fig. 7.11) with three PTFE rings in place, one for the displacer and two for the piston. This view also shows the spider that guides the end of the displacer tube. Next the bearing case with mounted crankshaft is installed (Fig. 7.12). The water pump and blower mounted on the bracket at the side of the engine were unsuccessful early attempts at self-powered auxiliaries. In Figure 7.13 the connecting rods for the displacer

A few minutes into the drive back to Dhaka I gritted my teeth, confessed that we had a problem, and explained that leaky coolers had prevented us from running the engine. I braced myself for Bruce's response, but he was gazing at something on the road ahead of us. After a pause he said, "Oh, that's no problem; we always have leaks in coolers at first. What

80

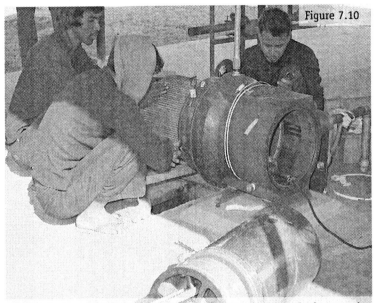
Figure 7.10

Bolting the hot end in place. The piston/displacer assembly is in the foreground.

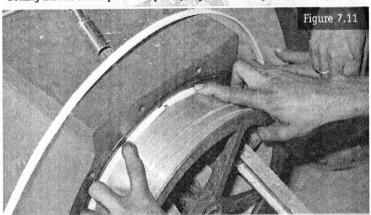
Figure 7.11

Installing the piston/displacer assembly in the engine. The piston, seen here, is fitted with two PTFE rings, the displacer with one. The spider, piston links, and displacer rod are visible.

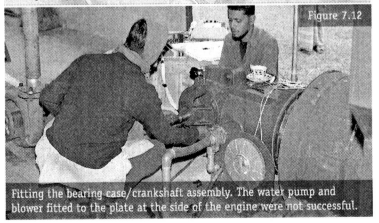
Figure 7.12

Fitting the bearing case/crankshaft assembly. The water pump and blower fitted to the plate at the side of the engine were not successful.

and piston are being connected. Figure 7.14 shows the assembled engine before the furnace has been slid into position.

IM-1 performance

In Figure 7.15 the engine is operating the No. 4 rice huller. While it was possible to mill rice, the varying load and tendency to jam made the huller inconvenient for routine testing. Generally the engine was belted to a water pump that provided a constant load (Fig. 7.16, 7.17). The flow of water from the pump provided a visual indication of the power of the engine (Fig. 7.18). Later we put together a Prony brake to measure actual power output (Fig. 7.19). The Prony brake was limited in that it could only be used for brief periods as the wood friction blocks would heat and begin to burn after only a minute or two.

As with the prototype, the auxiliaries were not yet integrated with the engine. Combustion air for the furnace was provided by an electric blower; cooling water came from a tap; and the engine was pressurized with our shop air compressor.

IM-1 problems

While many of the prob-

81

Figure 7.13

Connecting the linkage

Figure 7.14

The assembled IM-1 engine before moving the furnace into place

Figure 7.15

Milling rice with the IM-1 engine

lems of the prototype had been resolved in the design of the first intermediate model, some remained, new ones emerged, and we still had to deal with making the hot end and integrate the auxiliaries with the engine.

Although the displacer linkage had been strengthened, we had continued failures followed by redesigns and more failures. This went on till, at the end of the project, a completely new linkage design was adopted that eliminated the need for a bell crank altogether.

The leather cup seal on the crankshaft worked well for a while, but after the engine had been disassembled and assembled a few times it had to be replaced. A better sealing system was called for.

Mounting the engine to its foundation by its body made disassembly and reassembly simple but created a problem. With the crankcase extending unsupported from the body there was a lot of vertical shake that resulted in a rocking motion. One was made uncomfortably aware of the large unbalanced masses thrashing about inside the engine.

During testing we could see that there were problems with piston alignment, and in spite of our efforts the cylinder liner still became slightly oval. As for the cooler, we still had to figure out how to deal with leaking water.

Figure 7.16

The IM-1 engine ready to run the water pump

Figure 7.17

The IM-1 engine operating the water pump

Figure 7.18

The flow of water into the cistern gives an indirect indication of the engine's power.

Figure 7.19

A Prony brake fitted to the IM-1 engine.

Chapter 8
MAKING THE SECOND INTERMEDIATE MODEL

Crankcase

By January of 1984 design of the second intermediate model (IM-2) was under way with the help of a Styrofoam model (Fig. 8.1) to visualize one possible crankcase arrangement. In this model the crankcase was designed so that it could be conveniently mounted on a lathe for machining. At this time I felt there would be an advantage to operating the engine in a vertical position, and the crankcase was designed along these lines, though ultimately the engine was mounted horizontally, the same way as the prototype.

The crankcase casting was designed to have the cylinder of a small compressor mounted on it with its piston linked to the bell crank of the displacer drive. Figure 8.18 shows the compressor piston attached to the bell crank. This was a feature inspired by the Philips 102C gen-erator set, but in this case I totally under-estimated the pump capacity we would need to pressurize the engine. The little piston, about 40 mm bore, operating at 600-700 rpm, didn't come close to having the capacity to pressurize the volume of our engine's large working space and crankcase.

To machine the crankcase the base was first faced, and then the flange of the crankcase was turned on the large lathe (Fig. 8.2). The rest of the machining operations were performed

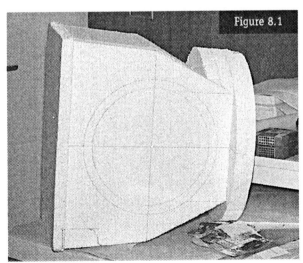

Designing the IM-2 crankcase

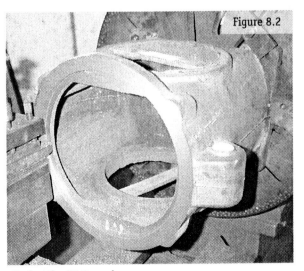

Facing the IM-2 crankcase

Mounting plate on the milling machine for the crankcase

Fly cutting one side of the crankcase

on the milling machine using a mounting plate on the milling machine table to ensure that the cylinder axis would be in line and perpendicular to the crankshaft axis (Fig. 8.3). As before, all of the facing, boring, drill-

The crankcase after the machining operations are completed

ing, and reaming operations were completed without shifting the crankcase casting on the milling table. Figure 8.4 shows the crankcase-mounted flange down on the milling table as one of its side ports is being faced with a fly cutter. In Figure 8.5 the finished crankcase is being marked out for drilling the holes for the bolts that will secure the cast-iron body/ water jacket to the crankcase.

Bearing case

The bearing case was similar to the one used in the IM-1, except that the crankshaft was fitted with two taper roller bearings, and the greased leather cup seal was replaced with a conventional automotive oil seal. This sealing system worked well and never had to be replaced during the numerous assembly/disassembly cycles the engine went through as other problems were sorted out.

Pre-heating the cast iron die for the cooler casting

Melting an aluminum ingot in the gas-fired crucible   Fluxing the molten aluminum

Cooler

I continued to try and get an aluminum cooler casting that had no porous spots. Rather than relying on the usual melts of scrap aluminum, I located an importer and convinced him to sell me a few ingots of pure aluminum even though these were usually sold only by the ton. In our final attempts we tried gravity die casting. In Figure 8.6 the cast-iron die, machined from a leftover IM-1 body casting, is being preheated. At the same time aluminum ingots were melted (Fig. 8.7), and we were being careful not to overheat the melt. After fluxing, the dross was removed from the molten aluminum (Fig. 8.8) and the aluminum was poured into the die (Fig. 8.9). The quality of our casting steadily improved, and though we never got one that was perfectly sound, they were good enough that we could make them leak-proof with a bit of epoxy.

Cylinder liner

The cast-iron cylinder liner of the first intermediate model had a wall thickness of 5 mm, but still it had become a little oval, so the thickness of the IM-2 cylinder liner

Pouring molten aluminum into the die

The cylinder liner casting was mounted on the large lathe and turned to its finished dimensions.

Turning the flange of the cylinder liner casting on the medium-size lathe

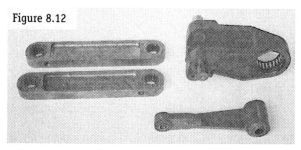

Mild steel piston links with needle bearings, the main con rod, and the swing link

Boring the seats for the wrist pins on the Model-B piston crown

was increased to 7 mm. After machining the flange of the cylinder liner on the medium-size lathe (Fig. 8.10) it was mounted in a jig on a face plate of the large lathe for the remaining turning operations (Fig. 8.11). Ports for air flow were milled with the milling machine, as was done with the IM-1 cylinder liner shown in Figure 6.16.

IM-2 piston linkage

The first piston links used with the IM-2 engine were machined from aluminum castings and fitted, with oil-impregnated sintered bronze bushes. These were not strong enough, and they were replaced with links milled from mild steel and fitted with needle bearings. Figure 8.12 shows the mild steel piston links along with the main con rod and swing link.

IM-2 piston

As the earlier one-piece (Model-A) piston was difficult to cast and machine, the IM-2 used a two-piece piston. In the first version (Model-B) the wrist pin seats were cast and bored in the piston crown (Fig. 8.13). This was a tricky operation as only one side could be bored at a time, and the piston then had to be rotated 180 degrees to bore the opposite side, with the risk of ending up with at least a slight misalignment.

There was still some binding of the piston due to misalignment, so I devised a different method of connecting the links to the piston. The casting for the crown of the Model-C piston was designed to be machined entirely on the lathe with a central seat for a mounting bracket (Fig. 8.14). The wrist pins for the

Turning the Model-C piston crown

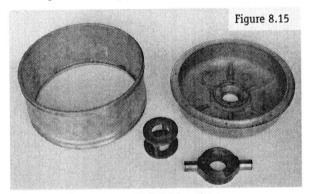

The parts that make up the Model-C piston

The Model-B (left) and Model-C (right) piston crowns

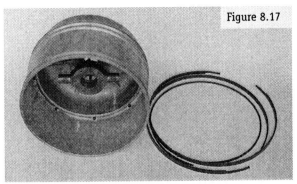

The assembled Model-C piston. The piston was fitted with two 10mm x 3mm PTFE wear rings (notched to prevent activation) and one 4mm x 3mm compression ring.

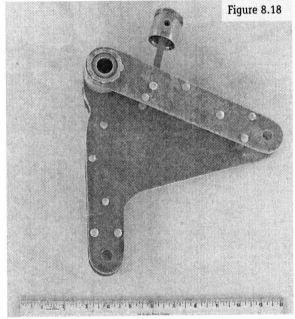

An off-set bell crank with a small (too small) compressor piston

piston links were machined from one piece of steel that was attached to the crown with a bracket, which had a little flexibility to accommodate minor misalignment (Fig. 8.15). The crowns of the Model-B and Model-C pistons are shown side by side in Figure 8.16. The assembled Model-C piston is seen in Figure 8.17 along with the carbon/graphite PTFE rings. Paper strips are used under the PTFE rings to adjust the clearance between the rings and cylinder.

By this time the virgin PTFE rings, which were cut from 1/8-inch sheet, had been replaced with 1/8-inch x 10 mm carbon graphite–impregnated PTFE rings made to order for us by a company in the USA. Both the Model-A and Model-B pistons had two PTFE wear rings that

89

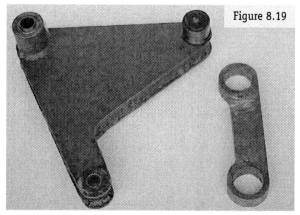

Figure 8.19

The last, and strongest, bell crank design of welded mild steel plate. The displacer con rod is machined from mild steel and is connected with heavy-duty cam follower bearings to the bell crank (shown here) and the crank-shaft throw (not shown here).

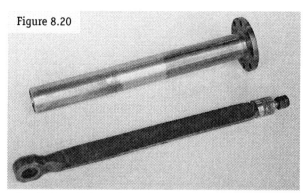

Figure 8.20

The displacer drive tube and flexible drive rod

doubled as compression rings. In the Model-C piston, the wear rings were notched so that they didn't act as compression rings, which may have been creating excess drag. For compression a third ring, just 4 mm wide, was located in a groove between the piston crown and skirt. This compression ring was activated from beneath by an O-ring.

IM-2 displacer linkage

Bell cranks and their con rods and bearings failed on a discouragingly regular basis. The prototype had used an aluminum bell crank (Fig. 4.22), which was not sufficiently durable. In our IM-1 engine I had designed an offset bell crank made of mild steel plate that was assembled with rivets and some welding (Fig. 6.29). The steel webs were perforated to reduce weight, so when this design failed, I made the next version without the perforations (Fig. 8.18). In these we used needle bearings to connect arms of the bell crank to the displacer con rod and to the displacer

rod. The inner races for these needle bearings were secured in place by bolts. The displacer con rod, which was initially cast iron, was attached to the crank throw with a conventional sealed deep-groove ball bearing.

After more failures, a much improved bell crank (Fig. 8.19) was made from welded mild steel plate. This bell crank was not offset and used bearings made from very durable cam followers to connect the displacer con rod to the crank throw and to the bell crank. The displacer con rod was now machined from mild steel.

Ultimately it was the displacer drive that proved to be, figuratively and very much literally, the weakest link in the design of the prototype and in our IM-1 and IM-2 engines. It was unfortunate that Jim Novak had so alienated William Beale at the start of the project that William stepped down as leader of the Sunpower team for our project. It was only in early 1986, as the project was drawing to a close and Dick Fuller had taken over as acting representative for the Asia Foundation in Bangladesh, that William agreed to come to Dhaka to review the design of the engine. This resulted in a radically changed design for our

Figure 8.21

The displacer

last engine that finally gave us the durability we needed.

IM-2 displacer

The design of the displacer remained pretty much unchanged from our IM-1 engine except for a larger-diameter displacer tube and heavier drive rod. Figure 8.20 shows the displacer tube with the flexible drive rod removed, and Figure 8.21 shows the displacer itself. In the beginning there were occasions when the displacer can started to collapse from the effects of heat and pressure, but our system of explosive forming and spot welding allowed us to put together a new displacer in a day or so. By adding more baffles and using thicker stainless steel sheet for the displacer can, the risk of collapsing was pretty much eliminated. By this time we were attaching the stainless steel displacer can to the cast-iron body with small hex bolts and, as before, sealing the joint with epoxy cement.

Explosive forming (Part 2)

The success of making the 0.7 mm-thick displacer domes and baffles using explosive forming encouraged me to scale things up

to form the 3 mm (1/8-inch) thick stainless-steel dome of the hot end. This required a significantly larger die, a bigger explosive charge, and a deeper tank.

Ship "breaking," or scrapping, is a big business in Bangladesh, and much of our raw material came from the marvelously well stocked scrap market in Dhaka. Mild steel in thicknesses ranging up to 2 inches and more could be cut to whatever shape we needed for less than a dollar a kilogram. Generally all the materials were of high quality, especially the stainless steel and bronze shafts. From the scrap market we procured a large mild steel water tank that was gas cut (Fig. 8.22) to give us a large open tank. This tank was buried in the ground and filled to the top with water.

The die was designed so that the explosively formed piece would give us both the hot end dome and the shoulder ring that connected the hot end can with the regenerator housing. The die was so heavy that we had to rig a chain hoist over the tank to lower it into position.

Gas cutting a tank from a scrapped ship to use in explosive forming

This 500mm x 3mm stainless steel blank was not fully formed by the explosion. Later, with a larger charge, the piece was fully formed.

In the first split second after the explosive is detonated, the water thrown out of the tank is still rising.

A second later, much of the water blown out of the tank drenched the surrounding area.

The fireworks supplier had said he could make a larger explosive to form the hot end, so we brought him to the project and demonstrated how we were forming the thin displacer domes. Then we showed him the 500 mm-diameter blank of 3 mm-thick stainless steel that we wanted to form. He studied it, thought a bit, and said he would make an explosive that we could try out. In due course the explosive was delivered.

From the outside it was a ball of jute twine about five inches in diameter, and if it had been colored black it would have looked as though it came straight out of a comic book. Soon we had fitted it with an electric fuse and impregnated it with candle wax to make it waterproof. After mounting the blank in the die it was lowered into the tank using the chain hoist. When the internal space had been evacuated we stepped back—far back—and I touched the leads from the fuse to the car battery. The resulting explosion heaved most of the water out of the tank upward in a thick column. Figures 8.23

and 8.24 show the column of water as it is still rising and then as it peaks. For a minute or so afterward, water that fell on the roof of the engine shed flowed off as though we had been through a heavy rainstorm. The charge was not quite large enough, and Figure 8.25 shows that the piece was nearly but not fully formed. In a day the supplier was back with a somewhat larger explosive that did fully form the blank. The cost for each of these "firecrackers" was Tk200 ($10).

Studded hot end

For the prototype, Sunpower had fabricated the hot end, tack-welded the external fins in position, and then tightly fitted the inner corrugated heat exchanger and liner. The assembly was then ready to be brazed. No furnace brazing facilities were available in Bangladesh, so we would have to set one up on our own. I was reluctant to tackle this rather daunting task and energetically looked for alternative ways of making the hot end. After studying some of the Philips patents for heat exchangers, I decided to try a hot end with a grooved internal heat exchanger and

Parting the piece that will be used for the dome of the hot end

Parting the piece that will be used as the shoulder between the heater can and the regenerator can

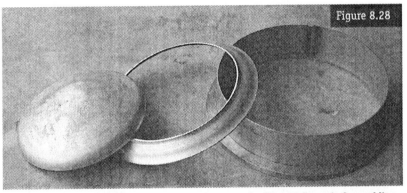

The hot end dome, shoulder piece, regenerator can, and mild steel flange before welding

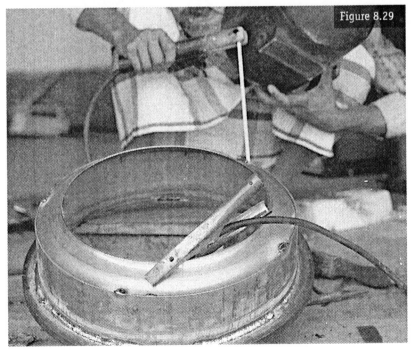

Welding the bottom parts of the hot end

welded studs for the external heat exchanger.

The explosively formed dome piece was mounted on the lathe face plate and the dome parted (Fig. 8.26), after which the shoulder piece was parted (Fig. 8.27). In Figure 8.28 the dome, shoulder piece, regenerator can, and mild steel flange are ready for welding. After welding the regenerator can to the mild steel flange the shoulder piece was welded in place (Fig. 8.29). The assembly was then mounted on the lathe, and the flange was turned to its finished dimensions (Fig. 8.30).

The heater can was made from ¼ inch–thick stainless steel plate that had been laboriously grooved on the milling machine (Fig. 8.31). The pattern of grooves was taken from an early Philips patent. After rolling, seam welding, and trimming on the lathe, the heater can was welded to the regenerator housing, and finally the dome was welded in place. Figure 8.32 shows how this was done on the lathe to ensure concentricity of the finished assembly.

The studs for the external heat exchanger were turned

Turning the flange of the hot end to its finished dimensions

The heater can has been rolled, seam welded, and welded to the regenerator housing of the hot end. Here the dome is about to be welded in place.

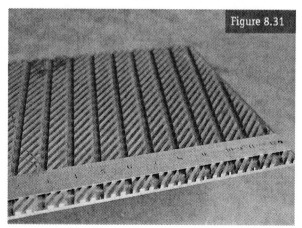

This quarter-inch stainless-steel plate was grooved on the milling machine to form the internal heat exchanger surface on the hot end can.

A close-up view of the stud welding head mounted on the drill press stand on the lathe cross slide

Operating the stud welder. The timer box behind my shoulder houses the heavy-duty relay that controls the arc welding machine that is connected to the welding head. The faceplate has been drilled with indexing holes so that each stud is accurately positioned.

The building that was constructed to house the brazing furnace. In the background is the smoke stack for the large steam engine that powers the hydraulic pumps for a set of jute presses.

The brazing furnace

Our first (and only) hot end with brazed heat exchangers inside and outside

from stainless steel rod. In order to weld them to the hot end I designed and made a stud welder from bits and pieces including a solenoid, some relays, a timer, and a drill press frame. To use the stud welder, a stud with a tapered end was put in the spring-loaded holder, which also formed the positive electrode of an arc-welding machine (Fig. 8.33), and was attached to the armature of the solenoid. The stud welder was lowered using the drill press handle till the stud contacted the surface of the hot end. The

95

The plain hot end fitted on the IM-2 engine before its first run. The shroud slides over the plain hot end and guides combustion gases close to its surface for effective heat transfer into the engine.

drill press was adjusted so that when it was at the bottom of its stroke the spring-loaded armature of the solenoid was compressed a little as it pushed the stud against the surface of the hot end. At this point a button was pressed that (1) closed a heavy-duty relay to start the welder, (2) activated the solenoid to raise the welding head, and (3) started a timer. As the welding current started to flow, the solenoid raised the welding head by a millimeter or two, striking an arc that was maintained for a second or two till the timer shut everything down and the spring-loaded armature thrust the stud into the molten surface of the hot end. By adjusting gaps, spring pressure, and time, it was possible for me to repeatedly get

good welds. The hot end was mounted in a jig on the face plate of the large lathe, and the face plate was drilled with indexing holes to correctly position the hot end as each stud was welded.

Although the stud welding proceeded quite quickly, there were an awful lot of studs, and I worked on it for several days and all of one night (Fig. 8.34) in order to complete the job with a minimum of distractions from other activities. Also I wanted to get the engine running before I left for China on June 20. There I was to give a paper on our project at the Second International Conference on Stirling Engines, which was held in Shanghai in 1984 from June 21-24.

Brazed hot end

In my desperate search for an alternative to furnace brazing I got myself into trouble. Bruce and Craig came for the six-month review in May of 1984, and at the start of our meeting with the Asia Foundation representative, Jim Novak, Craig expressed serious concern that work on furnace brazing hadn't started. I explained the reasons for trying alternatives and what we had accomplished, but Jim was adamant that work on brazing should be given the highest priority. I was puzzled with the concern Bruce and Craig had about brazing, since I had other options almost completed. Much later I realized that they were probably having to deal with the same brazing problem as the collaborative venture of Stirling Technology, Inc. and Stirling Dynamics in Madras that was being set up to manufacture an engine based on our design. Any experience we gained with furnace brazing in Bangladesh would be of help to them in Madras.

About this time Mrs. Pati suggested that she request Volunteer Service Overseas for a volunteer with a technical background to help us in the project. VSO, which is the British equivalent of the US Peace Corps, assigned Nigel Hargreaves to our project. This was a particular help when there were several different activities that had to be supervised at the same time. Nigel reported directly to Mrs. Pati, which kept her in touch with what we were doing.

The design of the brazing furnace was done by Nashir Hirge, whose family operated a large factory that manufactured various sorts of bricks. Figure 8.35 shows the building constructed to house the furnace. This was located next to another KWT jute press located on the other side of Narayanganj town. The furnace itself (Fig. 8.36) was gas fired with natural draft. During the first trial run of the furnace on September 19, 1984 we only reached 350 °C. By October 11th we were able to get 900 °C. Finally, after seven weeks of testing and fiddling, we were able to get the 1,100 °C that we needed to braze our hot end. After the hot end was fabricated with the external fins and internal corrugated heat exchanger tacked in place, the powdered nickel brazing material was mixed with a liquid plastic binder and applied to the joints, where it dried and held the brazing powder in place. The hot end was placed in a stainless steel retort that was purged with hydrogen and placed in the furnace. Hydrogen purging continued throughout the brazing operation. It took us eight hours to get the hot end up to the brazing temperature of 1,100 °C.

Finally we had our own locally brazed hot end (Fig. 8.37). The quality of the braze was not very good as there were many gaps where there should have been brazing material, but the hot end worked and was used on our engines subsequently. In hindsight the furnace should have been equipped with a forced draft burner. With bricks and ceramics the temperature in the furnace must be raised gradually, but in furnace brazing the temperature should be raised as quickly as possible. In the end only one hot end was brazed.

Plain hot end

Another alternative to brazing that I tried was a plain hot end. To make up for the loss of surface area by not having fins, the hot end was made 50 percent longer than the brazed and the studded hot ends. The plain hot end was very simple to make as nothing had to be done for the outside surface. Rows of stainless steel spacer tabs were welded around the inside of the hot end. The hot end was then mounted in a jig on the lathe so that the tabs inside of the can could be trimmed with a boring tool. After aligning the hot end flange, the tabs were trimmed till the inside liner could be slipped into place, leaving a gap of a few millimeters between it and the hot end can, through which the working air would shuttle back and forth. This ensured that the liner was correctly aligned with the axis of the cylinder and (hopefully) wouldn't touch the displacer when everything was assembled. Figure 8.38 shows the plain hot end mounted on the IM-2 engine.

Now that we were making our own hot ends, I fitted them with several flare fittings for ¼-inch copper tubing. Thermocouples with 1/16-inch stainless steel sheathing were led into the engine through short lengths of copper tubing. One end of the copper tube was pinched around the stainless steel sheath of the thermocouple and sealed at the end by brazing. The other end had been flared and fitted with a nut to make an airtight seal when the thermocouple was threaded into the hot end and fixed in place. The flattened copper tube served as a strain reliever, and I preferred this arrangement to the usual swage fittings. With these fittings we could finally monitor air temperatures wherever we liked inside the working space of our engines.

Regenerator

All of our engines used the same Metex regenerator material that had been used in the prototype. However, we had explored different ways that the regenerator could be made locally. One possibility was to procure the stainless steel wire and have it knitted for us by one of the local garment manufacturers. A second approach was to use stainless steel lathe turnings as regenerator material. Using surplus turnings was not feasible as the thickness was too great and normal cutting speeds on a lathe made the turnings brittle. We experimented with generating our own turnings by making very fine cuts on a stainless steel shaft using a liquid coolant. The quality of these turnings appeared quite satisfactory, though we never tested them in an engine. This method of making regenerator material would only be suitable where labor costs are low and conventional regenerator material hard to get or expensive.

Chapter 9

SECOND INTERMEDIATE MODEL ASSEMBLY AND PERFORMANCE

It was becoming a familiar scene. With deadlines approaching, the workers happily piled up overtime hours as they worked late into the evenings, and then there would be an all-night session or two. On June 17 we were up all night as we assembled the second intermediate model for the first time. At three in the morning of the 18th, after everything was together, we found that the piston was jamming, so the engine had to be stripped down to solve that problem. During the morning the reassembled engine was lifted into position with a chain hoist and bolted to its foundation. Next the furnace was slid into position and gaps plastered with mud to ensure that combustion gases only passed out of the furnace past the hot end. Finally connections were made for cooling water, furnace blower, and the compressor to pressurize the crankcase. At 12:05 p.m. on June 18, 1984, the IM-2 ran for the first time. We had enough time to open the engine, check that all was OK inside, and reassemble it in time for a demonstration run for USAID at 2:45 in the afternoon.

The next day, with a light heart, I flew with my wife, Sara Ann, from Dhaka to Bangkok and then on to Shanghai for the Second International Conference on Stirling Engines. While my presentation at the conference described our experience with the earlier IM-1 engine I was happy to report our successful first run of the IM-2 engine. It would not be long, however, before I was again immersed in problems of broken linkages.

Figure 9.1

All of the parts of the IM-2 engine spread out on the drying yard

Figure 9.2

The piston and displacer assembly of the IM-2 engine

IM-2 assembly

All of the parts of the second intermediate model are shown in Figure 9.1, where they have been spaced out on the drying yard. The 4 kg of Metex regenerator material has been removed, showing how the material on the hot side of the regenerator is discolored while that on the cold side is largely unaffected. Figure 9.2 shows the displacer with one PTFE wear ring and the piston with two wear rings. In Figure 9.3 the IM-2 is being assembled in the workshop before fitting the studded hot end. Some grinding of the studs on the hot end was required (Fig. 9.4) to get it to fit into the stainless-steel shroud that surrounds the hot end. The en-

Figure 9.3

Assembling the IM-2 engine with the studded hot end

Figure 9.4

Trimming the studs of the studded hot end. The proto-type hot end is in the foreground.

The assembled IM-2 engine

The displacer, piston, and their linkage

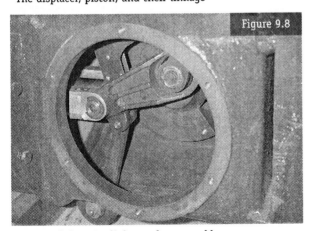

A view of the IM-2 linkage after assembly

Mounting the IM-2 engine on its foundation

The IM-2 crankcase cover (right) and the bottom of the blower housing

gine was assembled (and disassembled) in a vertical position (Fig. 9.5) and mounted on the foundation with a chain hoist (Fig. 9.6) before fitting the heavy flywheel. Figure 9.7 shows the displacer and piston with their links attached. Here the displacer and piston have been fitted with custom-made carbon/graphite-filled PTFE rings. The access port on the side of the crankcase facilitated assembly and inspection of the linkage (Fig. 9.8). It was even possible to run the engine at atmospheric pressure with the side port removed, at which times we could still hear the hiss of air leaking past the piston rings on each stroke. The leak sounded less serious than before, but it must still have been robbing us of a lot of power.

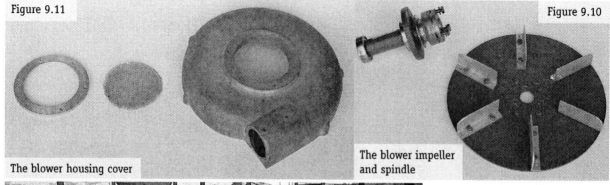

Figure 9.11

Figure 9.10

The blower housing cover

The blower impeller and spindle

Figure 9.12

IM-2 auxiliaries

The IM-2 crankcase cover (on the opposite side from the bearing case) supported the furnace blower. Figure 9.9 shows the crankcase cover (right) in which the blower shaft with its bearings are fitted, and the base of the blower (left). Figure 9.10 shows the blower impeller with its spindle and bearings, while Figure 9.11 shows the blower cover assembly. In Figure 9.12 the blower has been mounted on the engine. In operation the blower is first belted to the large hand-operated pulley for starting. After the operating temperature of the furnace is attained, the blower is belted to the jackshaft and is driven by the engine itself after removing the V-belt to the hand wheel. The jackshaft is driven by a V-belt connected to a pul-

The assembled IM-2 engine. The blower is operated by the hand wheel till the furnace is hot enough for the engine to drive the compressor through the jackshaft.

Figure 9.13

The engine with the piston, displacer, and hot end removed. The compressor mounted on the crankcase was a second unsuccessful attempt at a built-in compressor.

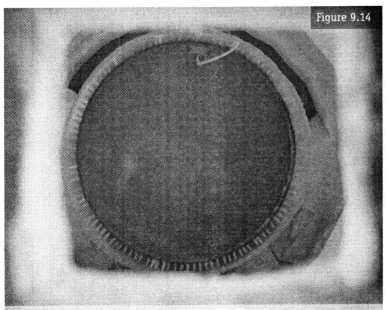

Figure 9.14

Looking in the port of the furnace while the engine is running. The thermocouple lead glows hot. The irregular heating of the fins most likely indicates gaps in the brazed joint between fins and the hot end.

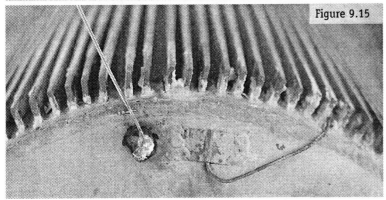

Figure 9.15

One thermocouple has been fitted under a tab that is tack welded to the dome. A second thermocouple has been brazed to the dome.

ley behind the flywheel. In the middle of the jackshaft is another pulley to drive the cooling water pump. In Figure 9.13 the cylinder of the unsuccessful built-in compressor can be seen on the top of the crankcase. The small cooling water pump sits to the right of the main water pump. The main V-belt pulley on the flywheel is used to operate the water pump; to operate the rice huller this is replaced with a flat belt

pulley.

IM-2 instrumentation

Temperature measurement
Type-K thermocouples were used to monitor temperatures. In the prototype there were no thermocouples leading into the compression or expansion space, so the temperatures of the air in the hot and cold spaces had to be inferred from external measurements. On the prototype hot end, thermocouples were attached to the dome and fins. In addition to these, the cooler water inlet and outlet temperatures were monitored.

When we began to make our own hot ends we incorporated fittings to lead thermocouples into the working spaces. In addition to external temperature measurements on the hot end, we eventually monitored temperatures at the following internal locations:

DI – Thermocouple brazed inside the heater dome

HA – Working air at the hot end of the heater

RH – Working air at the heater side of the regenerator

RC – Working air at the cooler side of the regenerator

CA – Working air entering the cylinder from the cooler

Figure 9.14 is a view into the hot furnace in which a glowing thermocouple can be seen. This thermocouple was held in contact with the hot end under a stainless-steel tab that was tack-welded in place. This arrangement gave a read-

Figure 9.16

The IM-2 engine fitted with the improved Prony brake. The pressure gauge can be seen at the top of the crankcase, where the compressed air line is attached. The jackshaft drives the blower for the furnace.

Figure 9.17

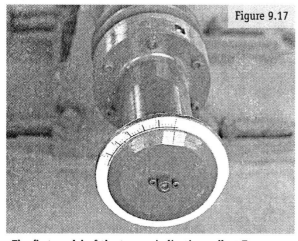

The first model of the torque-indicating pulley. Torque was read with a stroboscopic tachometer that simultaneously gave an rpm reading.

Figure 9.18

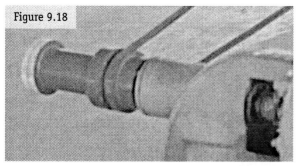

The second model of the torque-indicating pulley

ing that was too high, so another thermocouple was brazed to the hot end (Fig. 9.15) to get a more accurate reading.

As with the earlier engines, cooling water inlet and outlet temperatures were monitored. From time to time we would measure the rate of cooling water flow by recording the number of seconds it took to fill a one-liter container.

Pressure measurement. In all of our engines, crankcase pressure was monitored with a conventional pressure gauge fitted at the top of the engine. When the engine was running the needle oscillated rapidly, which gave us a rough indication of the maximum, minimum, and mean pressures in the crankcase of the engine.

Later a recording indicator device from a steam engine was adapted to trace a record of the pressures in the crankcase and in the working space of the engine. The recording drum was keyed to fit against and rotate with the

Recording temperatures, pressure, torque, and rpm during a run

View of the engine shed during a test run

end of the crankshaft. The pressure-actuated pen was connected through a T-connector and two line valves to both the crankcase and to the working space of the engine. To make a recording, the drum was held against the crankshaft, and as it rotated, the valve connecting to the crankcase was opened to activate the pressure recording pen. The pen was moved to contact the paper on the rotating drum for one or two revolutions to make the pressure trace for the crankcase. The operation was repeated for the working space so that the two traces were superimposed on each other.

Power measurement

In order to measure the power output of the prototype in Ohio, Sunpower had used a torque-indicating coupling between the engine and the pump, and this was connected to a computerized monitoring system. In our brief runs of the prototype engine in Bangladesh we had no means of measuring its power. For the IM-1 engine we made a Prony brake (Fig. 7.19), and later an improved Prony brake for the IM-2 engine (Fig. 9.16). With this arrangement we could get an idea of how much power we were getting, but our Prony brakes were limited to short runs. Another limitation: it was not possible to make power measurements while operating equipment such as the pump or the rice huller.

To enable us to get continuous readings of engine power, I designed a torque-indicating pulley for the water pump that was used in conjunction with a stroboscopic tachometer. Figure 9.17 shows an early configuration of the torque-indicating pulley, which was first used in late December 1984. The system was modified several times before we got the range and accuracy we required. Figure 9.18 shows the last version. This system enabled us to accurately monitor engine power during operation of the water pump over a wide range of speeds and power.

Analysis. To analyze the performance of the engine the following measurements were recorded by hand on a chart at five-minute intervals under the following headings.

Figure 9.22

Milling rice with the IM-2 engine

Figure 9.21

Radha is ready to brake the engine with a piece of wood to prevent over-speeding if the rice huller jams and the flat belt comes off the huller's pulley. Momotaz feeds rice husk into the combustion air as it enters the furnace.

DI – Temperature of heater dome (inside)

HA – Temperature of air in expansion space

RH – Temperature of air at heater side of the regenerator

RC – Temperature of air at cooler side of the regenerator

CA – Temperature of air in compression space

TEMP IN – Temperature of cooling water at inlet

TEMP OUT – Temperature of cooling water at outlet

LTR/MIN – Flow rate of cooling water

AIR PRES – Air pressure in the crankcase in bar (gauge)

RPM PUMP – Speed of the pump

TORQ – Torque reading at the water pump

 HUSK – Rate of rice husk consumption

At a later time these values were entered into an AppleWorks spreadsheet. Within the spreadsheet a number of calculations were made and the following additional figures were displayed and printed out.

H/R – Temperature drop across the heater (difference of HA and RH)

R/R – Temperature drop across the regenerator (difference of RH and RC)

RC – Temperature drop across the cooler (difference of RC and CA)

Figure 9.23

The IM-2 engine with the furnace removed

Figure 9.24

When the engine was running well, water from the pump reached the back wall of the tank.

KW OUT – Heat being rejected in the cooling water
RPM ENG – Speed of the engine
HP – Power output of the engine

One important additional figure calculated within the spreadsheet was the percentage of predicted power. This made use of William Beale's nifty formula for predicting the power that a Stirling engine can be expected to produce. In this formula a constant (the Beale Number) is multiplied times the piston's swept volume in cubic centimeters, the engine's speed in hertz, and the mean working pressure in bar. For a well-designed engine in which the hot end operates at 650 °C and the cooler at 65 °C the Beale number is 0.015.

Watts = 0.015 cc Hz Bar

A very well built engine of good design might produce twice this predicted power; a poorly designed engine might produce half or less.

For different heater and cooler temperatures the Beale number can be calculated as follows:

Beale No. = 0.034 – (0.052(Tc/Th))

Here Tc and Th are absolute temperatures (degrees Kelvin) in the cooler and heater where °K = °C + 273.

After an engine run was completed and the spreadsheet filled out, the actual power output for each data set was calculated from the entered figures for torque and speed. At the same time, using the Beale formula, the predicted power was calculated from the entered figures for speed, pressure, heater temperature, and cooler air temperature

along with the engine's swept volume (7,065 cc). A formula embedded in the spreadsheet compared the actual power to the predicted power, and the result was displayed or printed out as a percentage. Typically on a good run we would get something in the range of 50 percent of the predicted power.

In order to monitor the operation of the engine as the run was proceeding I used a hand calculator to calculate the percentage of expected power we were getting. If the percentage of predicted power started dropping I knew I had a problem inside the engine. Figure 9.19 shows our set-up for recording the operating data.

IM-2 operation

Figure 9.20 is a view of the engine shed during a test run in June 1984. It is interesting to see how much the Ipil ipil tree, planted as a sapling in January 1983 (Fig. 4.18), had grown in seventeen months.

Figures 9.21 and 9.22 show the IM-2 being used to operate the rice huller. As Abeda tends the rice huller Radha holds a piece of wood against the flywheel. If the rice huller jams (a common occurrence) the flat belt would slide off, the engine would run free, and Radha would brake the engine by levering the wood up against the flywheel to prevent over-speeding. By now we knew all too well that if the engine ran free, all of the power would be absorbed by the displacer and some part in the displacer linkage would surely break.

Rice husk is hand-fed by Momotaz through a funnel into the flow of air entering the furnace from the blower. By watching the exiting flue gases she was able keep the feed rate high enough so the engine ran well but not so high as to produce smoke. Monju weighs out 50-gram batches of husk as needed by Momotaz and notes the time each batch was used, so that we had an accurate record of fuel consumption throughout the run.

In Figure 9.23 the IM-2 is belted to the water pump. A smaller water pump driven from the jackshaft provides cooling water for the engine. When the flow of pumped water reached the back of the water tank (Fig. 9.24), we knew the engine was running well.

Fuel efficiency

An impressive aspect of the project's engine was its relatively good fuel efficiency. The calculations below are based on actual power and husk consumption figures over a period of twenty-five minutes from one of our test runs.

In rice husk 80 percent of combustible energy is in the form of volatiles and 20 percent is in the form of fixed carbon. In our cyclone furnace the husk passed through in only a second or two. In this short time the volatile components of the husk vaporize and burn completely, but there is insufficient time for the fixed carbon to burn. The fixed carbon in the form of rice husk char falls into the ash pit. The figure for "Unused energy" below refers to the energy remaining in the char.

Husk consumption rate. . . . . 15 kg/hr
Energy in husk . . . . .13 mJ/kg
Energy available . . . . .195 mJ/hr

Unused energy (20%) . . . . 39 mJ/hr
Heat generated . . . . 156 mJ/hr
Equivalent in kW (1W=1J/sec) . . . . 43.3 kW
Shaft power. . . . . 3.7 kW (4.9 hp)
Heat-to-power efficiency. 8.5%

The figure of 8.5 percent heat-to-power (thermal) efficiency is not bad for a small biomass-fueled engine in the first stages of development and better than would be expected from a steam engine of this size. No effort was made during this time to improve furnace efficiency as we were fully preoccupied with the engine itself.

It was clear that we were incurring significant losses due to piston and displacer ring drag and piston ring blow-by. By reducing these losses and with improvements in furnace efficiency with a simple combustion air preheater, it seems reasonable to expect that an overall thermal efficiency in the range of 10 percent to 15 percent would be attainable.

In our pilot rice mill a No. 4 steel rice huller operated by a 5-hp diesel engine had a milling capacity between 200 and 280 kg of paddy per hour. Husk makes up about 20 percent of paddy so that the production of rice husk would be 40-56 kg/hr. Under these conditions the Stirling engine's husk requirement of 15 kg/hr represented only 28 percent to 38 percent of the mill's husk production. This meant that availability of husk to fuel the Stirling engine would not be a problem.

By comparison, the specific fuel consumption of a 5-hp diesel engine is about 250 gm/kWhr, which gives an efficiency of 31 percent. Of course, diesel fuel is a refined product, and this figure for fuel efficiency does not take into account the energy expended in oil exploration, drilling and extraction, refining and transportation.

Production cost

An important objective of the project was that the Stirling engine should be competitive with diesel engines in respect to manufacturing cost. Because the Stirling engine would offer a savings in fuel cost we proposed that a realistic target selling price would be 50 percent more than the selling price of a comparable diesel engine. The local price of a 5 to 6 hp diesel engine at the time was Tk13,000 ($520), so a target selling price for the project engine would have been Tk19,500 ($780).

A study to determine the likely cost of production and the market demand for the husk-fueled Stirling engine was undertaken by a local consulting firm on behalf of the project. The estimates the firm arrived at for the cost of locally manufacturing the engine ranged from Tk7,890 ($700) to Tk25,000 ($1,000) depending on whether or not the raw materials used in manufacturing the engine were allowed the same concession on import duty rates that was allowed in the case of diesel engines imported for agricultural purposes.

Progress and problems

By the first part of 1985 there had been enough progress in our project that people, even those who were not mechanically inclined, were impressed to see the power we were extracting from rice husk. One of the most flattering compliments we got was from the Country Representative of the United Nations Development Program in Bangladesh. He had come to Narayanganj to meet Mrs. Pati in regard to some KWT activity that UNDP was supporting, and in the process had been brought by to see our project. He watched with interest as we fired up the IM-2 engine and started milling rice. It was a brief visit, but he asked a number of intelligent questions. Then as he was leaving he paused, looking at the running engine, and said, "You know, getting this power from rice husks is a little like splitting the atom, and what is better is that you don't produce any toxic wastes." I smiled; he had made my day.

We had now accomplished many of our technical objectives. We could make a Stirling engine in Bangladesh that could be operated using rice husk as its fuel. The engine was capable of producing the 5 hp required to operate a No. 4 steel rice huller. Our fuel efficiency was more than satisfactory as the engine used only a fraction of the husk produced in the milling operation. The auxiliaries (compressor, furnace blower, and coolant pump) had been integrated with the engine so that it was a stand-alone unit. Finally, the engine had been fully instrumented so that we could now accurately measure temperatures, pressures, speed, torque, and power output.

What we had not achieved was mechanical durability, and breakdowns were still a regular occurrence.

Chapter 10
NEW PHASES AND A NEW ENGINE

Our project was originally planned to run for three years, from July 1981 to June 1984. After being extended a couple of times the project was now scheduled to wind up in June 1985.

Bruce and Craig arrived on May 14, 1985 to participate in our final review meetings with USAID. This was their last visit to the project and they, with their new company, Stirling Technology Inc., were now fully involved in a collaborative business venture with Stirling Dynamics in Madras. Their objective was to manufacture and market a biomass-fueled Stirling engine, the ST-5, which was based on the RHEP prototype design.

In our meeting with USAID on May 23 we reviewed our budget and found that there would be enough funds to run the project a few months beyond the scheduled ending date in June. The extra time would be used to continue testing and de-bugging the engine and prepare a technical report giving details of the IM-2 design and what we had (and hadn't) accomplished up to this time. On May 27 Craig and Bruce headed to Madras to pursue their work on the ST-5.

On June 4, USAID informed us that there were sufficient funds to run the project another four months, which would take us through October. It was good to have this extra

time but posed a problem for my family, as it wouldn't cover schooling and housing beyond October. This gave us something to ponder as the school year came to an end in June.

Phases A and B

At the beginning of the summer holidays, many expatriate families were heading out of Bangladesh for home leave or to vacation spots. On June 13 my family and I joined the exodus and flew to Bangkok. The next morning at our hotel I received a call from the Asia Foundation's Bangkok office saying there was a message for me from Dhaka. It turned out to be a telex from Dick Fuller, and the news was good! USAID had found some funds that needed to be spent, and suddenly we had $200,000 for the project, more than enough to run it for another year. It felt like Christmas in June! Now I needed to write up a plan for what we would do during the next year.

The prospects now looked good for tackling the basic design problems that had been plaguing us. A few months earlier Jim Novak had left the Asia Foundation, and Dick Fuller had moved from the position of assistant representative to acting representative. With this change there was now a possibility that William Beale would be willing to come to

Bangladesh and participate in a review of the engine design. Bruce, who was still convinced that the original Ericsson configuration was adequate, was now busy in Madras and would not be involved in any future planning for our project. From the Asia Foundation's Bangkok office I began drawing up a plan of activities for the next year that would focus on the long overdue redesign of the project engine.

To identify this extension of the project as Phase 4 didn't seem appropriate, since we hadn't accomplished all the objectives that had been spelled out for the original Phase 2 and Phase 3. What emerged were Phases A and B.

Phase A (July 1 to November 30, 1985)

1. Continue testing the IM-2 engine.
2. Prepare the "RHEP Second Interim Report" with details of the design and operation of the second intermediate model engine.

Phase B (December 1, 1985 to May 30, 1986)

1. Review the current design and develop a new engine design that would resolve our problems with the weak linkages and the leaky cooler castings.
2. Make the new engine.
3. Organize a conference to present the results of our project and discuss the potential for biomass-fueled Stirling engines in the region.

A new engine design

William Beale had concurred that the project engine design needed to be changed, and he agreed to come to Dhaka to participate in this exercise. Joining him would be Owen (Rod) Fauvel who, besides having experience with Stirling engines, taught production engineering at the University of Calgary in Canada. William would provide the expertise to unravel the mysteries related to heat transfer and flow in the new design, and Rod would ensure that the new design would be mechanically durable. Our initial plan was to have the design review in November of 1985, which would give us six months to make the engine and make the first test runs. As it turned out, William and Rod couldn't work this into their schedules, so the design review was fixed for the end of January 1986, which reduced our time to make and test the engine to only four months.

William and Rod arrived in Dhaka on January 23, 1986. Initially I took them to Narayanganj, showed them our workshop and ran the IM-2 engine for them, first with the plain hot and then with our brazed hot end. Next we had initial meetings with the Asia Foundation and USAID. During these meetings I was gratified when William stated explicitly that the original design had intrinsic weaknesses and that I had been right, long before, in suggesting that the engine linkage should be redesigned.

The engine demonstrations and initial meetings took three days. For the next three days William, Rod, and I sat around a table on the veranda of my house in Dhaka brainstorming with paper, pencils, calculators, reference books, and numerous cups of coffee as we worked on the new engine design. It was an exciting time. By then I knew quite well what we could and couldn't make in our workshop, and I vetoed anything that involved unfamiliar manufacturing procedures or unproven engine designs. For these reasons some of the different design options we discussed were quickly discarded. These included:

- A Ringbom engine with a crank-operated piston and free displacer
- A Rider (2-cylinder) engine with a tape drive

Two design options were within our capabilities:

- The same Ericsson linkage of our earlier engines but with fully redesigned linkage and crankcase to give the required strength.
- A Rider arrangement (two cylinders and two pistons) with a Ross linkage.

William and Rod would have loved to make a Ringbom or tape-drive engine, but they agreed that the Ross arrangement would ensure that we got a durable drive in a design that was definitely within our capabilities to fabricate. Once this was decided, William and Rod sketched out the geometry of the Ross linkage with heavy-duty bearings.

The problems we had with our coolers related to our difficulty in obtaining the rather large (and expensive) aluminum castings of requisite quality from local foundries. In ad-

dition, the original design called for extensive machining to form the internal fins for the working air and external grooves for the cooling water. Recently Sunpower had achieved good results with coolers made from copper sheet, and William drew up a design for our new engine along these lines. In this arrangement one sheet of copper is rolled and the edges brazed to form a cylinder. Another thinner copper sheet is corrugated and soldered to the inner surface of the first piece. This assembly is slipped into a cast-iron cooler body that has been grooved to allow water to circulate on the outside of the cooler while providing a backing to support the thin-walled cooler against being deformed by the air pressure within the engine. O-rings seal the water out of the working space, while air within the engine flows back and forth through the internal corrugations.

After a final debriefing meeting with the Asia Foundation and USAID, William and Rod left Dhaka on January 30, leaving me with a sheaf of sketches containing detailed dimensions for the new cooler and Ross linkage mechanism. Rod was returning to Canada, and William flew to Madras to visit the Stirling Technology/Stirling Dynamics operation there.

William had been staying with us during this visit, and on the day of his departure, as usual, we had breakfast on our veranda. As we waited for the toast to brown, William seemed preoccupied. He said, "You know, this Ross design is much better that the original Ericsson design. Would you object if I discuss it with Bruce and Craig in Madras?"

I assured him that this would be fine since the whole purpose of our project was to develop and introduce a viable Stirling engine and make the design available to any interested party.

William thought some more and said, "Of course, they are pretty far along with the Ericsson design and probably couldn't justify to their investors a radical change at this stage. You are lucky to be able to change the design at this point."

It may have been too late to change course in Madras, or Bruce may have insisted on sticking with the original design. In any case, the ST-5 eventually emerged on the market with the Ericsson linkage.

The Ross linkage

The engines that the Stirling brothers developed all had a single power piston. In Robert's engines there was a single displacer operating in the same cylinder as the piston. But when James introduced the use of pressurized air within the engine in 1827 he arranged the displacer in a separate cylinder and eventually had two displacers connected through air ducts to opposite sides of the piston, making it double acting.

In the early 1870s in New York, Alexander K. Rider introduced a new mechanical arrangement in which there were two pistons, a hot piston and a cold piston, operating 90 degrees out of phase with each other. The hot piston had a cap, much like a displacer, to separate the air in the hot end from the oil-lubricated hot piston. In Rider's engines both cylinders were arranged vertically below the crankshaft and connected to

cranks (90 degrees out of phase) on opposite sides of the flywheel. These engines were bulky and heavy for their power, but they were very durable and easy to operate on wood, coal, kerosene, or gas. Thousands of these engines were made during the late 1800s, many of them being used to operate pumps for domestic water supplies.

Starting in 1971, Andy Ross of Columbus, Ohio designed and made a number of small Stirling engines with the objective of producing an engine that could produce one "person power," about 50-100 watts. After experimenting with several rhombic drive engines Andy turned his attention to other arrangements, including Rider's two-piston configuration. In 1976 Andy came up with a simple and elegant mechanism, now known as the "Ross linkage," in which the connecting rods of the hot and cold pistons are attached to two arms of a triangular yoke. A single crank throw and one end of a "rocking lever" are connected along the centerline of the yoke and the opposite end of the rocking lever pivots around a fixed point in the crankcase. With this arrangement Andy was able to get the required phase difference between the movement of the hot and cold pistons and at the same time reduce the lateral movement of the connecting rods almost to zero. It is this configuration that we would use in our next engine.

Making the Ross engine

From February 1 I closed the project workshop and worked at home on design drawings, and on February 22 delivered the first drawings (for the crankcase) to the patternmaker. More drawings followed, and on March 10 the

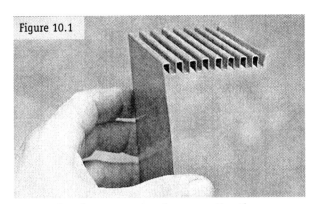

Figure 10.1

A test piece from our system for corrugating the copper sheet for the internal heat exchanger of the new cooler design

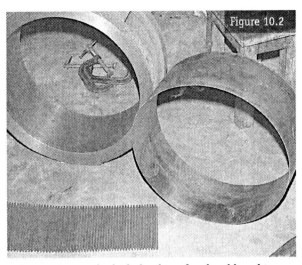

Figure 10.2

The cast-iron cooler body has been faced and bored to fit the copper cooler sleeve, which has been tinned with solder. One of the two pieces of corrugated copper sheets lies in front.

project workshop opened and began to bustle with activity. For a little over two months, with a holiday break for ten days, the workers' day started at 7:00 a.m. and ended at 10:00 p.m. The workers were happy with the overtime pay, and I was happy with the resulting speed that work got done. In the morning I would arrive with a handful of drawings and get things started. By mid-afternoon I returned to Dhaka to buy materials, hardware or tools that we needed. I would also visit the patternmaker and foundry as drawings were transformed to patterns, and patterns were transformed to castings. Finally I would head home to work on drawings till midnight. Early the next morning I headed back to the workshop with the latest drawings, hardware, and castings. I felt like the fairytale cobbler who had elves making shoes for him overnight. What had been sketches, raw metal, and rough castings the previous day would now be finely finished components sitting completed on the work table or mounted on a machine tool ready for the next operation. Soon the drawings for this day, materials and castings were in the hands of the workers for them to work their magic on, and I headed

back to Dhaka to repeat the cycle.

When I got around to buying the copper sheet for the cooler it was April 14, and there was less than a month to go before we were to have our end-of-project conference! To make the cooler we had to develop some new procedures. We made a jig for corrugating the sheet for the inner part of the cooler. Figure 10.1 shows our first test piece. After forming the outer sleeve by rolling and brazing a butt joint, the inside surface was tinned with solder. The internal corrugation was likewise tinned with solder where contact would be made with the sleeve. Figure 10.2 shows the tinned sleeve, the cooler body, and one of the two corrugated sheets that would be soldered to the inner surface of the sleeve. In Figure 10.3 the completed cooler has been disassembled to show the cooler sleeve and reveal the internal grooves through which water circulated from an upper (visible) manifold to a lower manifold. William had come up with a truly nifty design that was

Figure 10.3

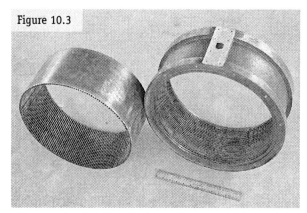

The completed cooler. The internal corrugated heat exchanger has been soldered to the copper sleeve. The cast-iron body has been grooved for cooling water and two O-rings. Cooling water flows from a lower manifold (not visible) through drilled holes to the internal grooves. After flowing in the grooves around the copper cooler sleeve, the water leaves the cooler through the upper manifold.

Figure 10.4

The cooler installed on the engine. Air passes from the regenerator through the cooler and then into the cold cylinder through the two ports at the bottom.

relatively easy to make. It was also less expensive and far more efficient that the earlier aluminum cooler, and best of all it didn't leak! The working air passed from the regenerator through the cooler and into the cold cylinder through two ports (Fig. 10.4). The space between the hot cylinder and the cooler was filled with a thick cast-iron "stuffer" sleeve to minimize dead space and direct the flow of air from the cold side of the regenerator to the cold cylinder (Fig. 10.5).

I designed the Ross engine with two bearing cases and two nearly identical crankshafts that coupled together at the center to form one unit. This way I could have two counterweights and there would be no overhung rotating or reciprocating parts, but this added to the steadily increasing weight of the engine. In Figure 10.6 one of the crankshaft assemblies has been exploded to show all of the components, including the bearings, the lock nut, and the pressure seal with its housing. As in the IM-2, the pressure seal was a conventional spring-activated automotive oil seal.

Figure 10.5

The cooler with the hot piston cylinder and stuffer installed

Figure 10.6

One of the two bearing cases with the crankshaft removed to show the taper roller bearings, lock nut, pressure seal, and seal housing

Figure 10.7

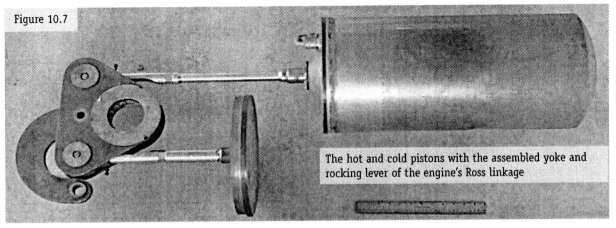

The hot and cold pistons with the assembled yoke and rocking lever of the engine's Ross linkage

The Ross linkage reduces the lateral movement of the end of the connecting rods to such a degree (in our case about 5 mm) that connecting rods were fixed to the pistons; there were no wrist pins. This meant that the pistons rocked a little during a stroke, but this was acceptable if w e used a single compression/wear ring. Figure 10.7 shows the piston assembly along with the assembled yoke and swing link. The large bearing in the center ran on the crank throw, and the bottom bearing on the swing link was pivoted in the crankcase. The displacer had an aluminum body as we wanted to make the mass of the hot and cold pistons equal. A snifter valve in the base of the hot piston maintained the highest cycle pressure in the hot piston to avoid it being crushed by the pressure swings inside the engine.

In Figure 10.8 the crankcase has been mounted on its foundation along with the "middle piece" and the cold cylinder. One bearing case has been installed with its half of the crankshaft and the flywheel. The yoke is partially assembled showing the swing link. In Figure 10.9 the pistons have been installed along with the cooler, and the yoke is fully assembled. The hot piston protrudes out of the engine to the right. The completely assembled engine with its plain hot end, compressor, and furnace blower is shown in Figure 10.10. In Figure 10.11 the engine is running as Momotaz feeds rice husk to the furnace by hand.

Figure 10.8

The crankcase with the middle piece and cold cylinder. One bearing case with its crankshaft and the flywheel has been installed. The yoke is being assembled showing the rocking lever attachment.

Figure 10.9

Assembly of the yoke and pistons has been completed. The hot piston extends beyond the cooler.

Figure 10.10

The assembled Ross engine with the furnace blower and compressor belted to the engine. The plain hot end has been fitted with several fittings that lead thermocouples to different locations in the working space of the engine.

Figure 10.11

Running the water pump with the Ross engine

Chapter 11
THE END OF THE PROJECT

The final activities of the project were to host an international conference to present what we had accomplished during our project, to run the Ross engine and evaluate its performance, and discuss with USAID about how to proceed with the introduction of the engine design.

Conference and first run

The conference was scheduled from May 11-14, 1986. In addition to presenting the results of our project, we would discuss the potential for biomass-fueled engines in the region. During the course of the project we had received a number of inquiries from organizations and individuals in different countries. Some of these people were themselves involved in projects related to renewable energy, and it was from among these that we invited nine to participate in our conference, the project covering all of their costs. There were two participants each from India, Nepal, and the Philippines, and one each from Sri Lanka, Thailand, and China. In addition to those coming from abroad, a number of people from organizations, institutions, and government agencies within Bangladesh were also invited.

The international participants arrived the afternoon of Sunday, May 11, and we had an informal welcome for them in the evening at the Sheraton Hotel, where they were staying. Ideally, by this time the new engine would have been completed and running. As it turned out we were still assembling the engine till 2:30 the morning of the 11th. After a short nap at Narayanganj, I drove home to clean up and go to the Sheraton Hotel to welcome the participants. Then it was back to Narayanganj to work all night to finish assembling the engine.

On Monday the 12th the first item on the conference agenda was a visit to Narayanganj to see our engines and workshop facilities. The guests arrived by bus at 10:00 in the morning, by which time the Ross engine was assembled and ready to make its first run. After a tour of the workshop we opened both the Ross and IM-2 engines to show the different linkages. We then fired up the IM-2 engine and demonstrated it, first pumping water and then milling rice. At this point we took a break for a lunch hosted by Mrs. Pati and this was followed by our first discussion session. During this time the workers shifted the furnace and the water pump from the IM-2 to the Ross engine to get it ready for its maiden run. By mid-afternoon our group returned to the engine shed for the first trial of the Ross engine.

There was a lot of excitement to be on hand for the first run of new engine design.

While preparations for this first run were going on, the skies turned black and in minutes we were hit with the full force of a Bangladeshi northwester. These brief but violent storms are brewed by cold fronts that sweep down from the Himalayas in the month of May before the onset of the monsoon. We carried on and got ready to start the furnace with an electric blower. Since the Ross engine had not yet been fitted with a hand-operated pulley to operate its own blower, we used an electric blower for the furnace till the engine could be started and run its own blower. Then our luck took a turn for the worse—the electricity went out. This wasn't a problem at first, and we soon had the furnace going with a blacksmith's hand-operated blower. In ten minutes or so the temperature of the hot end was up to 600 °C, the big moment had arrived, and the engine was cranked over several times. Nothing. My hopes of seeing the new engine spin to life on the first try faded away. We kept the hand blower going and raised the temperature to 650 °C and tried again. This time the engine turned over a few times before stopping. By now it was pouring rain and hail clattered on the corrugated roof of the shed. Undaunted, we boosted the hot end temperature to 750 °C and tried again. Now the engine responded by turning over several times before slowing to a stop. If we had electric power we could have pressurized the engine a little with the shop compressor to get it started, but since the power was still out it was clear that we weren't going to get the engine started on this day, so we called it quits and shut the furnace down.

I was disappointed, of course, but as it turned out, not too embarrassed. Most of the onlookers were involved in developing new technologies and understood the slim chance for getting a successful first run of a newly designed engine. This was the first day of our conference sessions, and there would be time on the third day for another visit to the project site. With electricity for the compressor and a bit of tweaking, the chances were good that the group would be able to see the engine running.

The storm subsided, and at 4:00 p.m. we all returned to Dhaka. After dinner at the Sheraton Hotel with the group, I headed back to Narayanganj to spend the night there and investigate why the engine hadn't started.

As I checked the engine, it appeared that there was some ring drag, so we removed the pistons and increased the clearance between the piston ring and cylinder of the two pistons by removing one of the paper packing strips under the PTFE ring for each piston. When the engine was back together again, I turned in for the night.

On Tuesday the 13th I had to get back to Dhaka to be on hand at 9:00 a.m. when the conference sessions resumed. We had not had time to try and run the engine, and as I was getting into the car to leave, Monsur suggested that the workshop crew could try and start the engine while I was at the conference. I was horrified! None of our engines had been run without my being present, and to try for a first run without my being on hand? But this was not an ordinary situation, and I knew that the workers knew as much, if not more, about running these engines as I did. After only a short pause I agreed and headed for Dhaka.

Back at the Sheraton Hotel we continued with the second day of the conference. Shortly before we broke for lunch I was called out for a telephone call. It was from Narayanganj and the news was good. By pressurizing the engine to 1 bar, the workshop crew had got it started easily and had run the engine for five minutes before it slowed and stopped. I returned to the meeting and happily reported that we had a first run. I was pretty sure that the engine had stopped as the aluminum body of the hot piston warmed up, expanded, and increased ring drag. This would be easy to fix, and we planned for the group to visit Narayanganj again the next day, this time hopefully to see a running engine.

Once again we were out of luck. In the afternoon we heard that on the following day, Wednesday the 14th, there would be a country-wide hartal (strike) from 6:00 a.m. till 12 noon. During this time, shops would be closed and no vehicles could ply the roads. This meant that we would have to shift our morning meetings to the afternoon, and there would now be no time left for participants to make a second visit to our project site.

There was a silver lining to this cloud, however. By starting at 4:45 in the morning, I was able to drive to Narayanganj before the hartal began and had the morning to work on the engine. During this time we disassembled the engine, removed another paper spacer strip from under the PTFE ring on the hot piston, and soon had the engine back to-gether again. This time, to our joy, when we started the engine it kept running. Because of an air leak, the engine's compressor could not maintain pressure in the engine, so we had to keep the shop compressor connected and running. The leak was so bad that with the shop compressor running continuously we could not keep the pressure in the engine to more than 1 bar. In this way we ran the engine for 30 minutes and were able to make our first power measurements. The power was low, around 1½ hp, but we could now get on with de-bugging the engine and monitor our results by keeping track of the power output.

At noon, when traffic started moving again, I returned to Dhaka for our meetings in the afternoon. Again I could report good news, but as most of the conference participants were leaving the next day to return to their respective countries, they would not be able to see the engine running firsthand.

The final session of the conference was a panel discussion entitled "The Regional Future of Stirling Engine Development." By this time the conference participants were quite enthusiastic about the prospects for Stirling engines in the region and pointedly asked the representative from USAID/Dhaka what plans were in the pipeline to carry on the work. The representative from USAID was noncommittal.

Final runs

After the conference was over I concentrated on running and de-bugging the engine. There was only two weeks before the end of the project on May 31, so there were only a

Figure 11.1

Getting ready for one of the final test runs of the Ross engine, the furnace is started with an electric blower. Once started the air hose will be connected to the engine-driven blower. Air from the compressor passes through a dryer before entering the crankcase. The device next to the air compressor is a modified steam engine indicator. When it was pressed against the end of the rotating crankshaft, traces could be made of pressure changes in the working space and in the crankcase.

few runs. But during this time we tracked down and solved a number of problems, and the power output of the engine steadily increased. We found that the air was leaking from the engine into the cooler and quickly fixed this with slightly thicker O-rings. I was suspicious that we had too much dead space, so I lined the plenum space between the regenerator and the cold cylinder with gasket material to reduce its volume. On the next run we were rewarded with a 10-percent increase in power.

Figure 11.1 shows the Ross engine during one of its test runs. The maximum power we were able to get up to this time was about 4 hp, which was enough to produce a good flow of water from the pump (Fig. 11.2). With more time the prospects were good that we would have been able to achieve 5 hp.

The most impressive feature of the Ross engine was its smooth and silent operation. When the prototype and our earlier engines ran there was always a fair bit of noise from the linkage, which I found unsettling. With the Ross engine, the bearings that Rod Fauvel had selected were massive, and this had

Figure 11.2

Water pumped by the Ross engine

paid off. During a run of the Ross engine the main sources of noise were the blower, the compressor, and the flow of water from the pump into the cistern. Because of the large amount of heat stored in the walls of the furnace it was possible to disconnect the furnace blower and the compressor and run the engine for 10-15 minutes on this residual heat. When we did this the only discernable noise was from the flow of water into the cistern. Standing with one's back to the engine it was not possible to tell if it was running or not. I had the comfortable feeling that this engine could run forever.

Future plans

Some months earlier in one of our project review meetings with USAID, the Asia Foundation and Kumudini Welfare Trust, we had discussed whether the project should again be extended after May of 1986. For different reasons we decided against this. By now Mrs. Pati felt that is was unlikely that Kumudini could effectively become involved in a manufacturing venture, and that there was not much else in the project that would be of benefit to the Trust. Unlike Jim Dillard, Dick Fuller thought the Asia Foundation should concentrate on its traditional scholarly activities, and he was anxious to conclude the

Figure 11.3

The workshop crew. From left to right in the front row: our rice millers, Momotaz, Zaiful, Monju (manager), Nurjahan, and Abeda. Back row: Nurul Amin (helper), Radha (milling machine), Fazul (fitter), Merrick, Monsur (turner), Dulal (welder), and Sainullah (turner).

project with our conference. I felt that if we succeeded in getting a reliably running engine it would be better to develop a new project in which we paid Kumudini for the use of the facilities and focused on working with local manufacturers. So there was no plan to extend the existing project beyond May 31.

On May 22, after we ran the engine in the morning, I returned to Dhaka for a 1:30 p.m. meeting with people at USAID. Now that we finally had a reliably operating engine I was optimistic about the prospects for a new project to get it manufactured and field tested. As the meeting got under way I happily described our success with the engine and the bright prospects for its future development. But it was to no avail. I was informed that the U.S. government no longer had funds for renew-

able energy projects, so there was no question of a new project, or even an extension to the existing project. I had been so immersed in making the Ross engine that I had not done a good job of keeping in touch with the people at USAID. If I had, there might have been a chance of continuing the project or at the least I would have been aware of how dim the prospects were. I was crushed.

In the remaining days of the project I was able to run the engine three more times before we closed the project down and handed everything over to Kumudini Welfare Trust. They eventually used the workshop to produce manually operated water pumps. As the project ended we took a final group photo (Fig. 11.3) of the workshop crew.

Chapter 12
POSTSCRIPT

After returning to the U.S. in June, I spent four months tromping around Washington, D.C. visiting various development organizations and government agencies in an effort to get funding to continue the work on our engine. Again I found that funding priorities had changed. A few years earlier "appropriate technology" had been the buzz word, and it was during this time that we were able to secure the funding for our project. Now, in the summer of 1986, funds were being channeled into programs that strengthened private enterprise and the transfer of off-the-shelf energy technologies such as wind generators and photovoltaics. There was a lot of interest in a biomass-fueled engine, but everyone wanted one that was ready to put on the market.

Even if an organization had been willing to fund further work on the Ross engine, I still had a problem. How could I convince someone to put up money to finish the development of our rice husk–fueled engine when a similar engine was going into production in India? While the Ross engine was certainly more durable, it was also heavier than the ST-5 and would cost more to produce. In October, as it began to get cold in

Figure 12.1

The compressor cylinder of the ST-5 is built into the spider that guides the end of the displacer rod. The compressor piston is fixed to the displacer rod (not shown) and doubles as a gas spring to reduce the load on the displacer linkage.

Figure 12.2

Starting an ST-5 at Auroville using firewood as the fuel

the U.S., I headed back to Bangladesh to pursue other directions in rural technology.

The ST-5

The ST-5 produced by the Stirling Technology/Stirling Dynamics collaboration in Madras did eventually go into production and generated a lot of interest.

To reduce the load on the displacer linkage, Bruce incorporated the engine's compressor with the displacer rod. Figure 12.1 shows the compressor cylinder (which is part of the spider) along with the compressor piston and the main piston assembly. The compressor piston, which is fixed to the displacer rod (not shown), has three functions: (1) it guides the tail of the displacer rod; (2) it functions as the piston of the compressor; and (3) it serves as a gas spring, which reduces the load transmitted from the displacer to its linkage. This is a good solu-

tion if the compressor is well maintained. If the compressor is allowed to wear, the effect of the gas spring is reduced and the displacer linkage becomes overloaded.

A number of the ST-5's were sold internationally. One was set up for extensive testing with a wood-chip gasifier in Switzerland. The Indian government's Department of Non-conventional Energy Sources financed between fifty and a hundred of the ST-5 engines. A survey carried out in India by Energy Consultants in 1988 mentioned that thirty-six engines were distributed for evaluation to institutions and, at a subsidized cost, to some individuals. Most of these engines were run briefly and then kept on display or put into storage.

To my knowledge, the most extensive use made of an ST-5 in India was in Auroville near the ex-French colony of Pondicherry in south India. Here Johnny Allen replaced the

An ST-5 with the furnace pulled back

5-hp diesel engine that powered the water pump for Fertile, one of the many small groups that make up the international community at Auroville. Johnny's focus is on sustainable living, and with the exception of the diesel pump he was able to avoid the use of non-renewable resources. He used a wood-fueled ST-5 Stirling engine to replace the diesel engine that powered his pump. The pump was run for an eight-hour day twice a week throughout the year. On the days that he pumped, he filled the tank for their domestic water supply, provided water for the farm animals, and irrigated their extensive garden. For a year the engine ran without mishap, but then some fixes were needed. As running time accumulated, more elaborate fixes were needed, and after three years the ST-5 was retired and the diesel engine reinstated. Later Johnny located and bought several used ST-5s that he has used

for parts or for low-power applications (Fig. 12.2). Most recently he runs a small grain grinder and a wet grinder once a week for a few hours (Fig. 12.3 and 12.4). As before, the fuel is firewood. Because the power requirement is low, perhaps 1 to 1½ hp, the engine is not pressurized and the stress on the displacer linkage is much reduced, so the prospects for a long running life are good.

A rhombic drive?

Over the years since the rice husk project wound up, I have made a number of Stirling engines, and after a while I concentrated on engines with two cylinders in a 90-degree V configuration. After dealing with the massive imbalances in the RHEP engines, I was attracted to the intrinsically good balance of the V-2 design. Then in October of 2000 I experienced what, if this were a religious

Operating a wet grinder with a wood-fueled ST-5. Power is sufficient to run both grinders at the same time.

matter, might be termed a "conversion." I was still in Dhaka, and in a day or two would be showing my workshop and current projects to a visitor. In my workshop, taped to a board on the wall behind my lathe, was a CAD assembly drawing of my latest V-2 gamma engine. It was a mass of lines that I could decipher but which would make no sense to anyone else, so I decided to clarify things by adding hatching to different parts of the drawing and then print a clean copy to put up on the board.

As I turned in for the night I reached for my bedside reading, which was *The Philips Stirling Engine* by Hargreaves. I wanted to check the excellent drawings in that book and use them as a guide when I would try to enhance my drawing with hatching the next day. I had already been through most of the book, some parts many times, and I quickly found a drawing of one of the Philips rhombic engines that would serve as a good ex-

ample for me to follow. As I scrutinized the drawing with a magnifier and then re-read various bits of text, it was as though many pieces of a puzzle had suddenly fallen into place. The rhombic drive would eliminate most of the problems I had been tussling with over the years. The price was a high part count, but that was a reasonable price for the other advantages. Within days I was designing a rhombic engine using the cooler, displacer, and hot end from the V-2 gamma engine, the rest of which was scrapped.

The first try at running this engine was midnight on June 12, 2001. The engine started on the first try and ran for an hour and twenty minutes at 260 rpm with low power till I removed the charcoal from its burner. It was just in time, because after many years in Bangladesh I was shifting to India. The workshop had been sold, and we were leaving Dhaka in a little more than a day.

If I were to set about making the RHEP engine today, I would stay with the plain hot end and the copper sheet cooler, but I would use a rhombic drive with the piston and displacer oriented vertically. This beta arrangement (piston and displacer in one cylinder) minimizes dead space; the vertical orientation would almost eliminate the considerable ring drag encountered with the piston and displacer in a horizontal orientation. With a well-balanced rhombic drive the operating speed could probably be raised to well above 700 rpm, the point at which the Ericsson engine began to shake badly. Another feature that bears consideration would be a speed-governing system.

The demand for a biomass-fueled Stirling engine for developing countries is as great now as it was in the 1980s—even more so as the price of crude oil steadily increases. Perhaps it is time to waken the sleeping beast.

REFERENCES

1816, Stirling, Robert
"Improvement for diminishing the consumption of fuel and in particular, an engine capable of being applied to the moving of machinery on a principle entirely new"
English Patent 4081

1827, Stirling, Robert and James
"Certain improvements in air engines for the moving machinery"
English Patent 5456

1840, Stirling, James and Robert
"Certain improvements in air engines"
English Patent 8652

1845, Stirling, James
Lecture
Proceedings of the Institution of Civil Engineers
Vol. 4, 355-361

1979, Beagle, Eldon C.
"Rice Husk Conversion to Energy"
FAO Agricultural Services Bulletin No.31
FAO, Rome

1979, Lockwood, L. Merrick
"Rice Hulls as a Source of Power for Small Rice Mills in Bangladesh"
AATC Information Bulletin No.6, Appropriate Agricultural Technology Cell,
Bangladesh Agricultural Research Council
Dhaka, April 1979

1979, Beale, William T, & L. Merrick Lockwood
"The Stirling Engine as a Power Source for Developing Countries"
The Asia Foundation, Dhaka, October 1979

1980, Walker, Graham

Stirling Engines
Oxford University Press

1981, Energy from Rice Husks 1981-1984
(TAF/Rice 388-0045-07)
The Asia Foundation, Dhaka, June 1981

1981, Ross, Andy
Stirling Cycle Engines
Solar Engines, Phoenix

1982, Notes of Meeting August 17 and 18, 1982 in Athens, Ohio, in connection with Bangladesh Energy from Rice Husks Project
by Doris Bebb, TAF/San Francisco

1982, Lockwood, L. Merrick
"First Interim Report, Rice Husk Energy Project (Phase I)"
The Asia Foundation, Dhaka, August 1982

1982, Wood, J. Gary, Bruce J. Chagnot, Lawrence B. Penswick
"Design of a Low Pressure Air Engine for Third World Use"
17th Annual Intersociety Energy Conversion Engineering Conference
Los Angeles, August 1982

1983, Energy from Rice Husks, Phase II
Planning and Evaluation Meeting Report
The Asia foundation, Dhaka, 25 November 1983

1984, Lockwood, L. Merrick
"Development and Field Testing of a Four Kilowatt Rice Husk Fueled Hot Air Engine"
2nd International Conference on Stirling Engines
Shanghai, June 21-24, 1984

1985, Lockwood, L. Merrick
"2nd Interim Report, Rice Husk Energy Project"
The Asia Foundation, Dhaka, November 1985

1988, Energy Consultants

"Report on Diagnostic Study of Gasifier & Stirling Engine Systems in India"
Bhopal, India

1991, Hargreaves, C. M.
The Philips Stirling Engine
Elsevier

1995, Sier, Robert
Rev Robert Stirling
Inventor of the Heat Economizer and Stirling Cycle Engine
L.A. Mair, Essex

APPENDIX
Index to Design Drawings

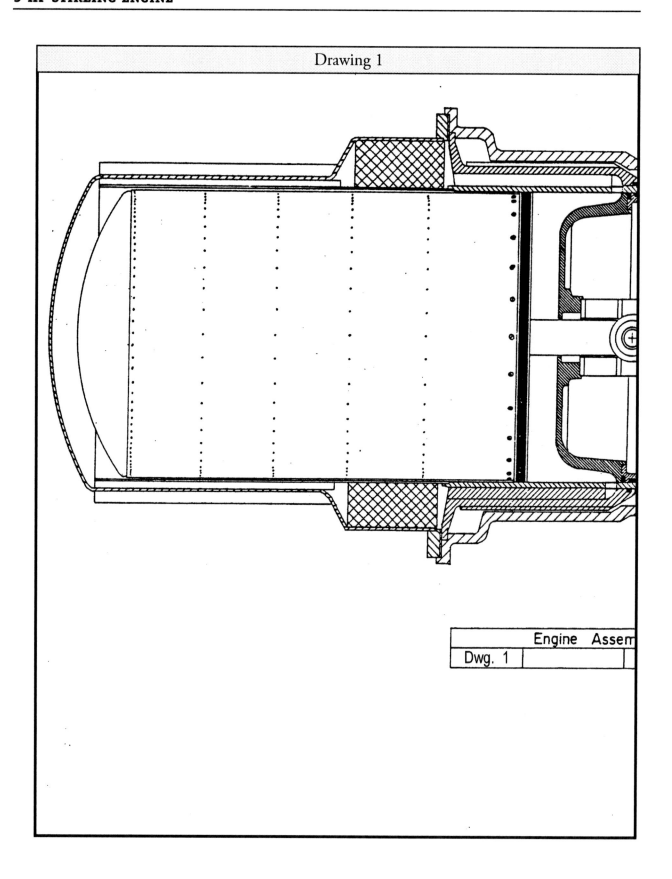

Drawing 1

Engine Assem

Dwg. 1

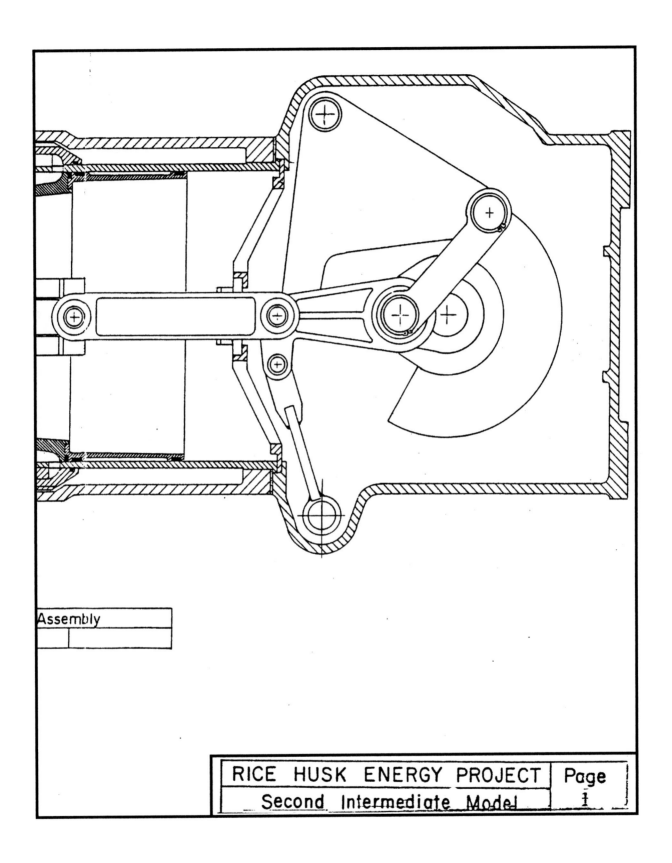

Assembly

RICE HUSK ENERGY PROJECT	Page
Second Intermediate Model	1

Drawing 2

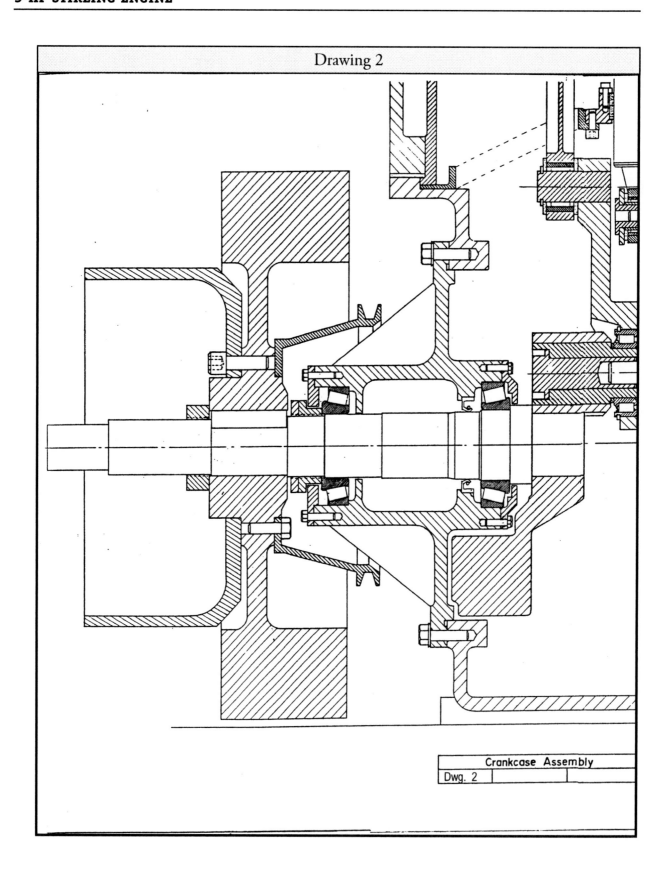

Crankcase Assembly		
Dwg. 2		

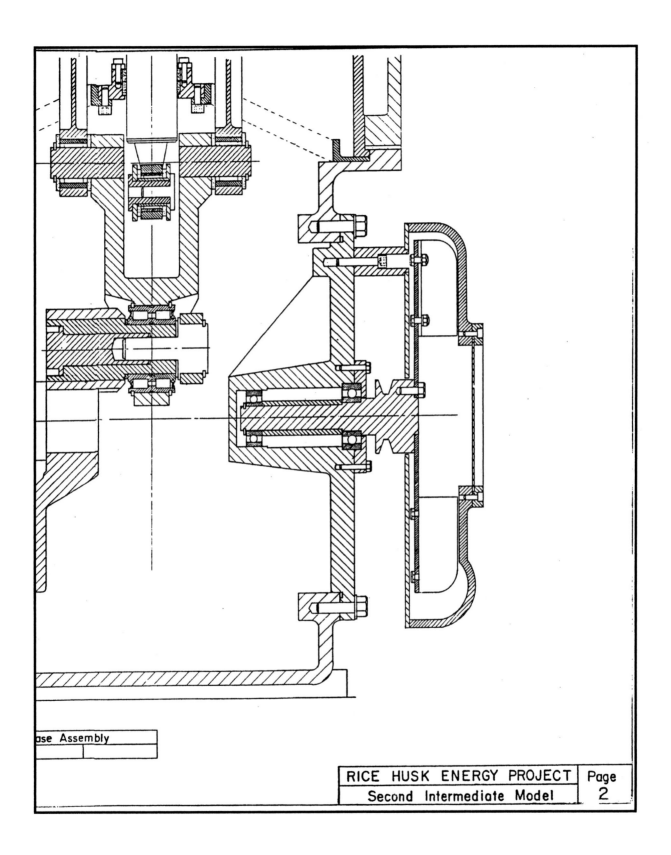

ase Assembly

RICE HUSK ENERGY PROJECT | Page
Second Intermediate Model | 2

Drawing 3

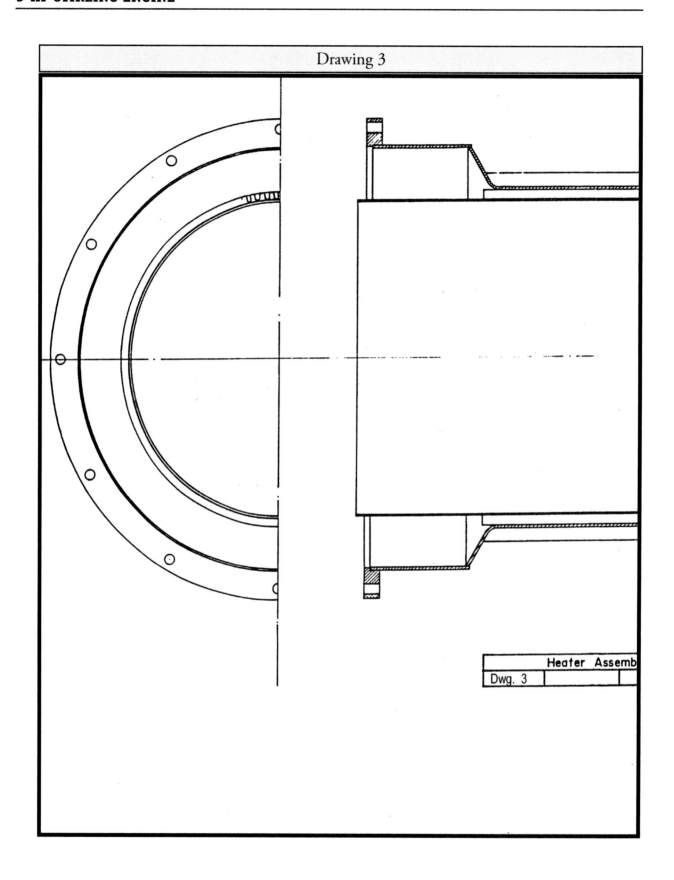

Heater Assemb

Dwg. 3

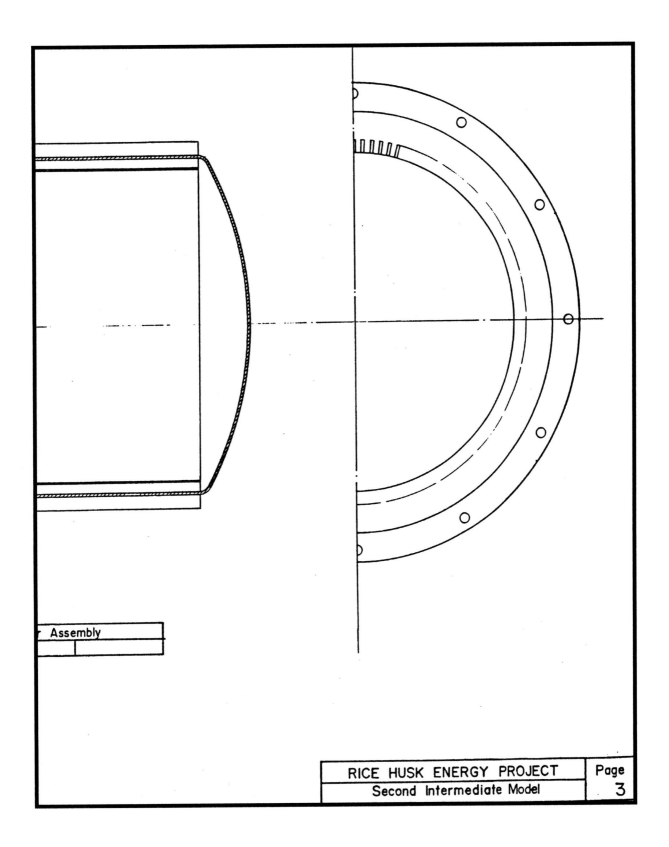

Assembly

RICE HUSK ENERGY PROJECT
Second Intermediate Model

Page
3

Drawings 4a, 4b, 4c

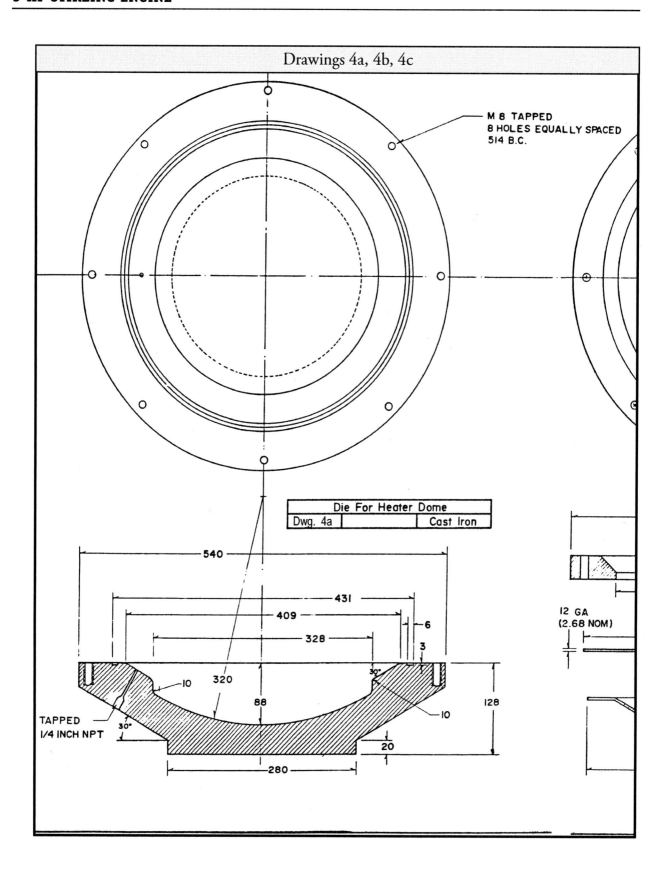

M 8 TAPPED
8 HOLES EQUALLY SPACED
514 B.C.

Die For Heater Dome		
Dwg. 4a		Cast Iron

540

431

409

328

6

3

320

88

128

30°

10

10

TAPPED
1/4 INCH NPT

30°

20

280

12 GA
(2.68 NOM)

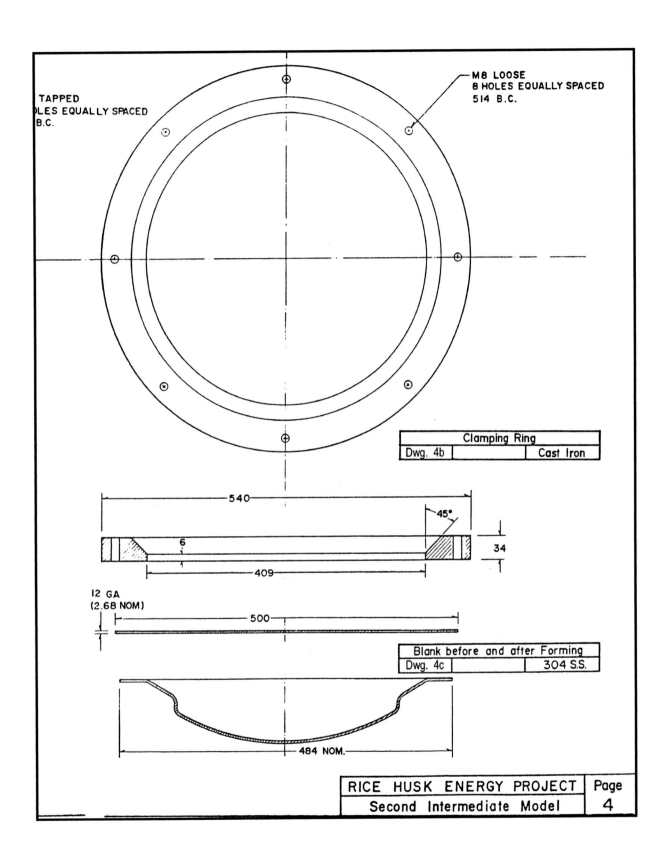

TAPPED
OLES EQUALLY SPACED
B.C.

M8 LOOSE
8 HOLES EQUALLY SPACED
514 B.C.

Clamping Ring		
Dwg. 4b		Cast Iron

540

45°

6

34

409

12 GA
(2.68 NOM)

500

Blank before and after Forming		
Dwg. 4c		304 S.S.

484 NOM.

RICE HUSK ENERGY PROJECT	Page
Second Intermediate Model	4

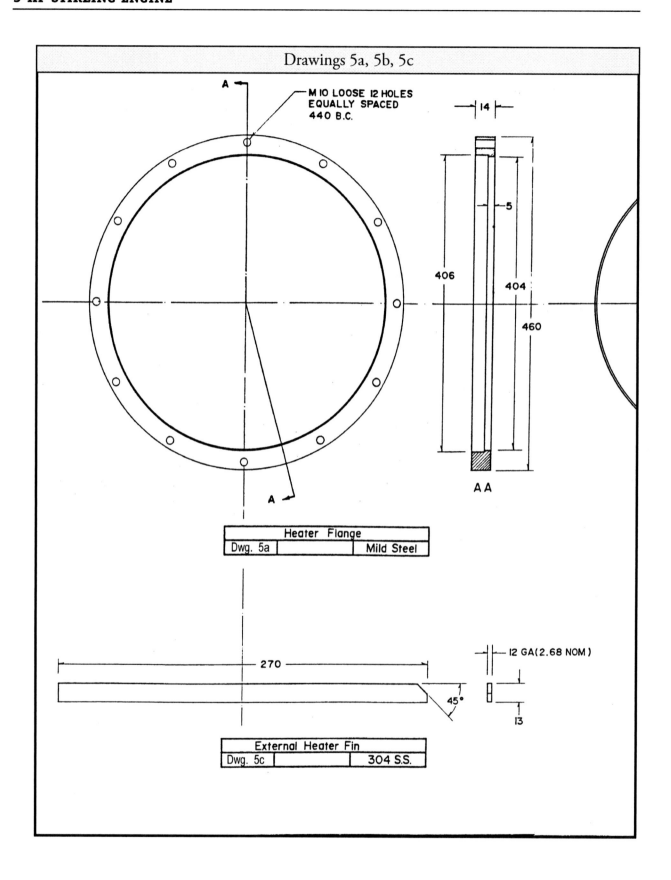

Drawings 5a, 5b, 5c

M 10 LOOSE 12 HOLES
EQUALLY SPACED
440 B.C.

Heater Flange		
Dwg. 5a		Mild Steel

External Heater Fin		
Dwg. 5c		304 S.S.

142

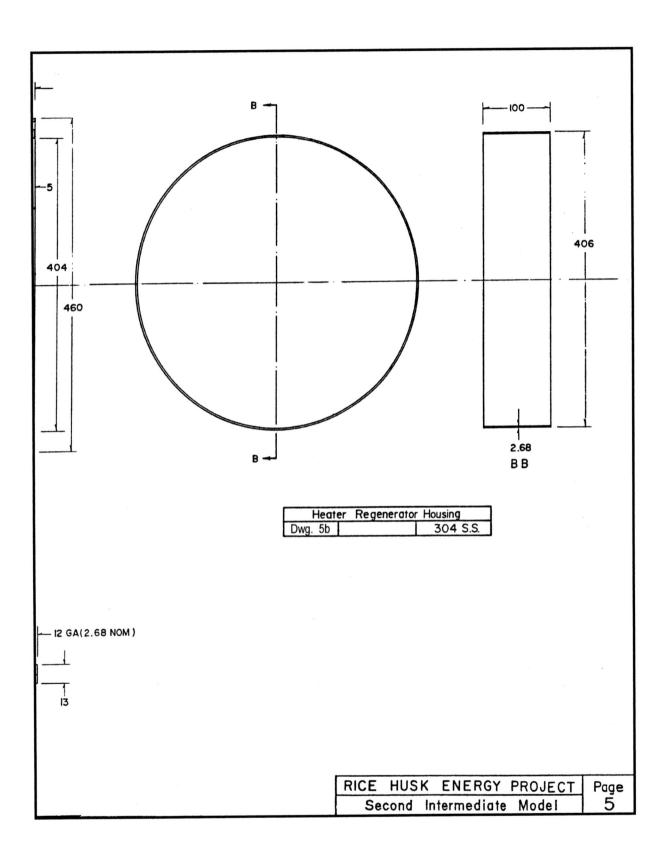

Heater Regenerator Housing

Dwg. 5b		304 S.S.

RICE HUSK ENERGY PROJECT

Second Intermediate Model

Page 5

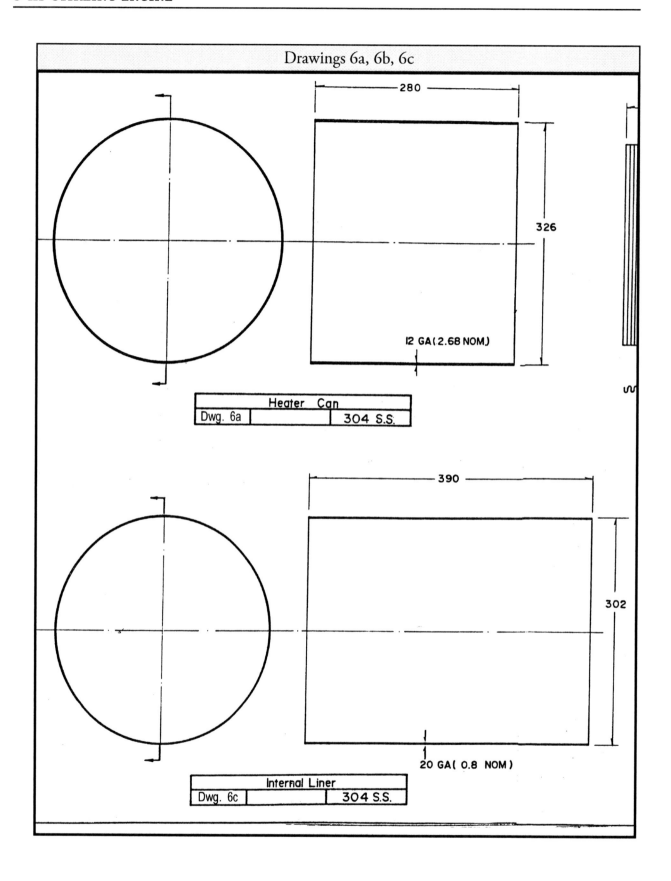

Drawings 6a, 6b, 6c

Heater Can		
Dwg. 6a		304 S.S.

Internal Liner		
Dwg. 6c		304 S.S.

144

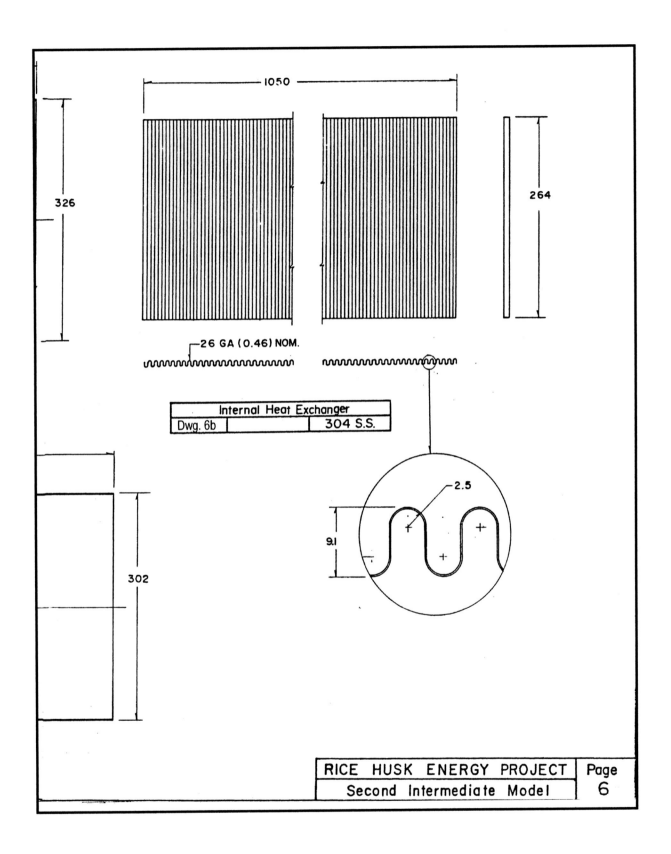

1050

326

264

26 GA (0.46) NOM.

Internal Heat Exchanger		
Dwg. 6b		304 S.S.

2.5

9.1

302

RICE HUSK ENERGY PROJECT	Page
Second Intermediate Model	6

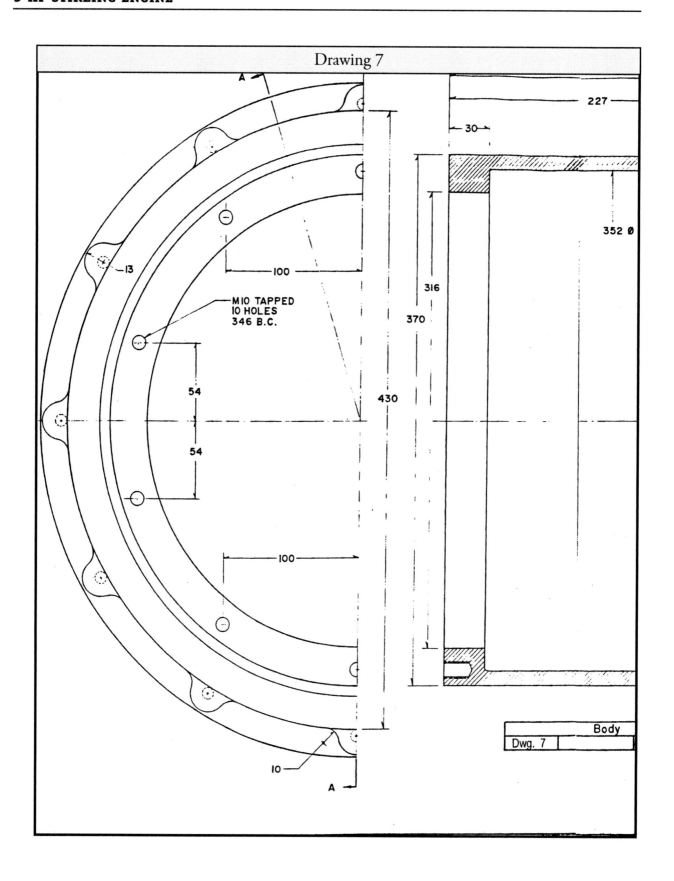

Drawing 7

A

227

30

13

352 Ø

MIO TAPPED
10 HOLES
346 B.C.

100

316

370

54

430

54

100

10

A

Body

Dwg. 7

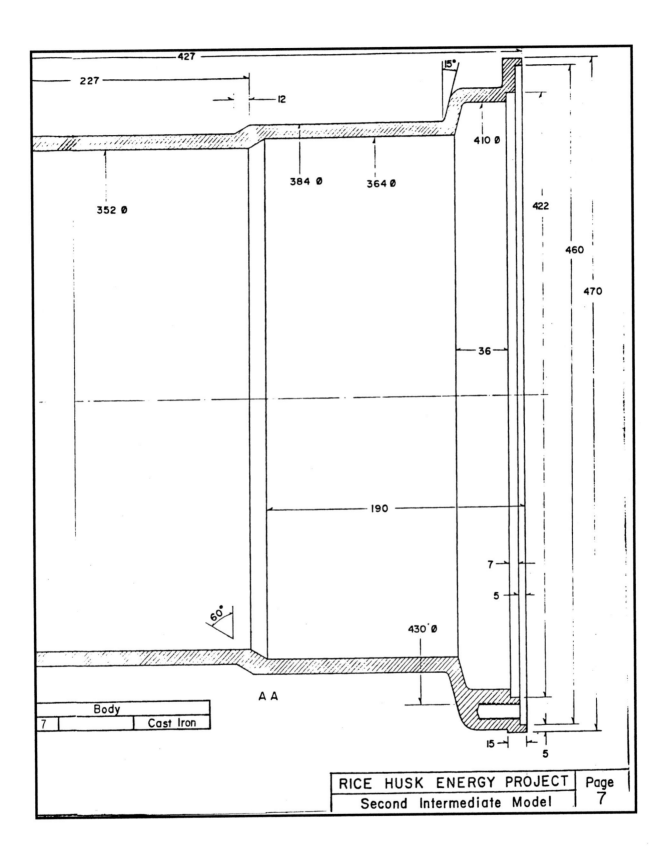

RICE HUSK ENERGY PROJECT | Page
Second Intermediate Model | 7

Body
7 | | Cast Iron

A A

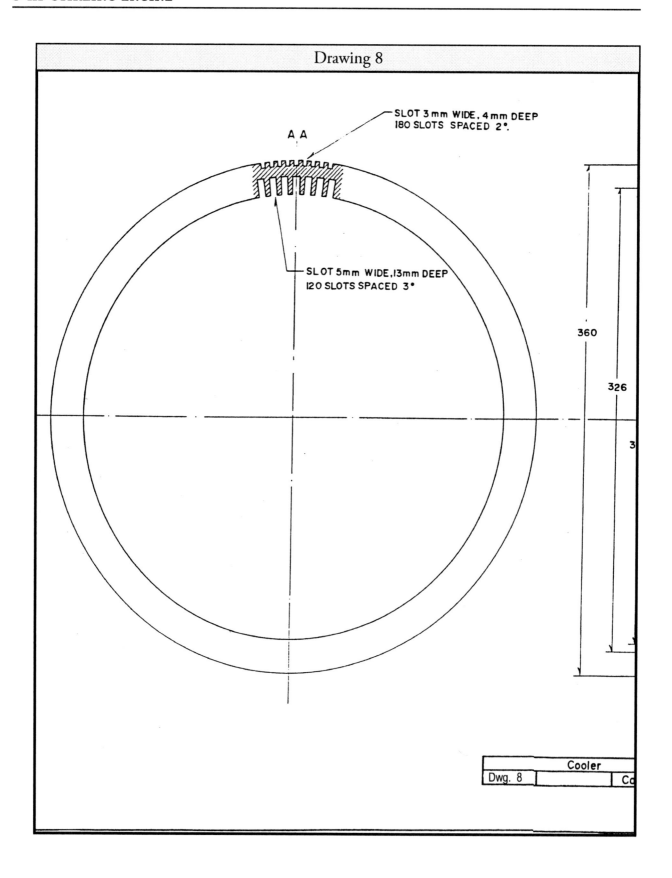

SLOT 3 mm WIDE, 4 mm DEEP
180 SLOTS SPACED 2°.

A A

SLOT 5mm WIDE, 13mm DEEP
120 SLOTS SPACED 3°

360

326

3

Cooler

Dwg. 8

148

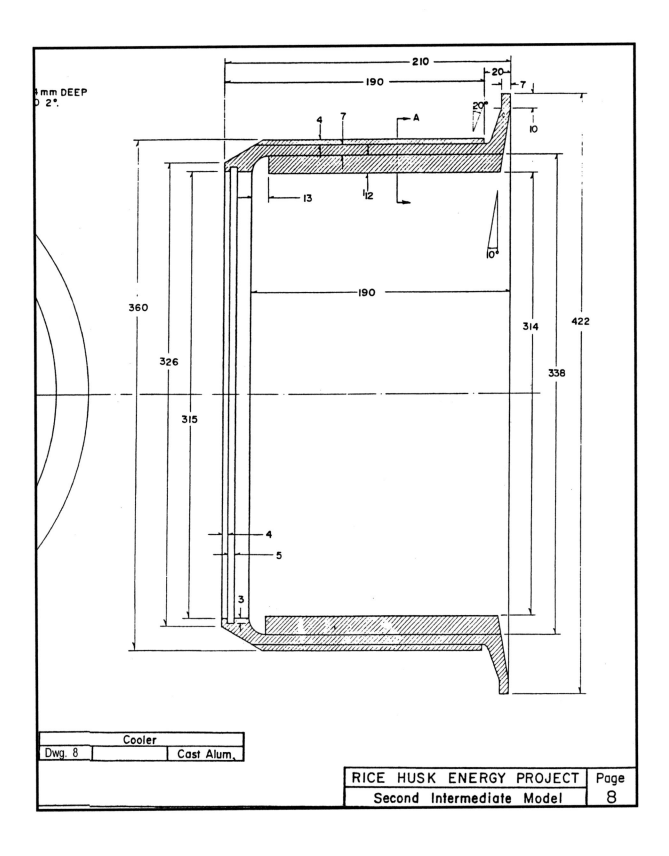

Cooler

| Dwg. 8 | | Cast Alum. |

RICE HUSK ENERGY PROJECT
Second Intermediate Model

Page
8

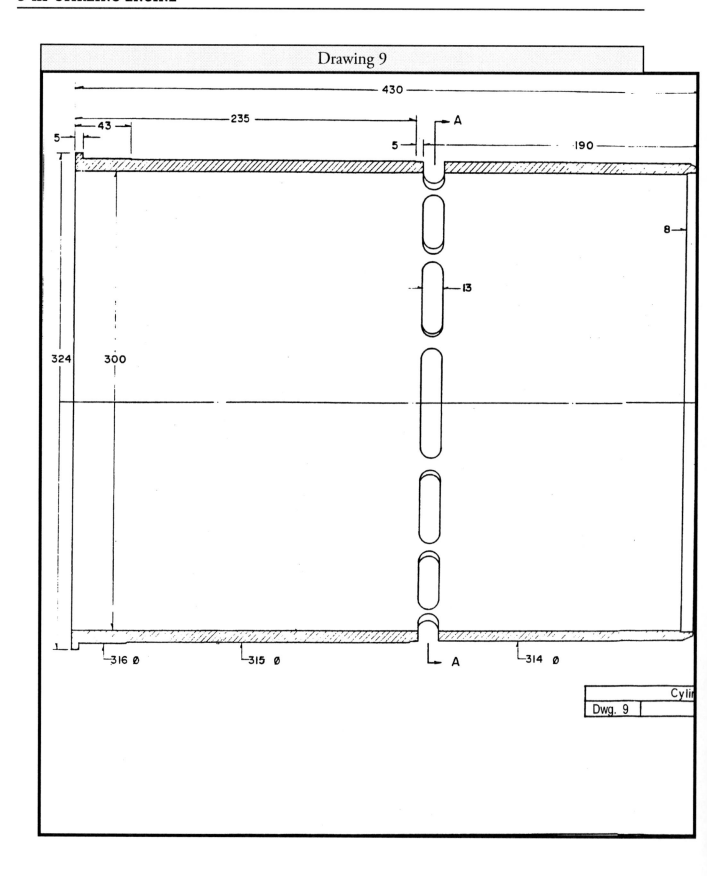

Drawing 9

Dwg. 9

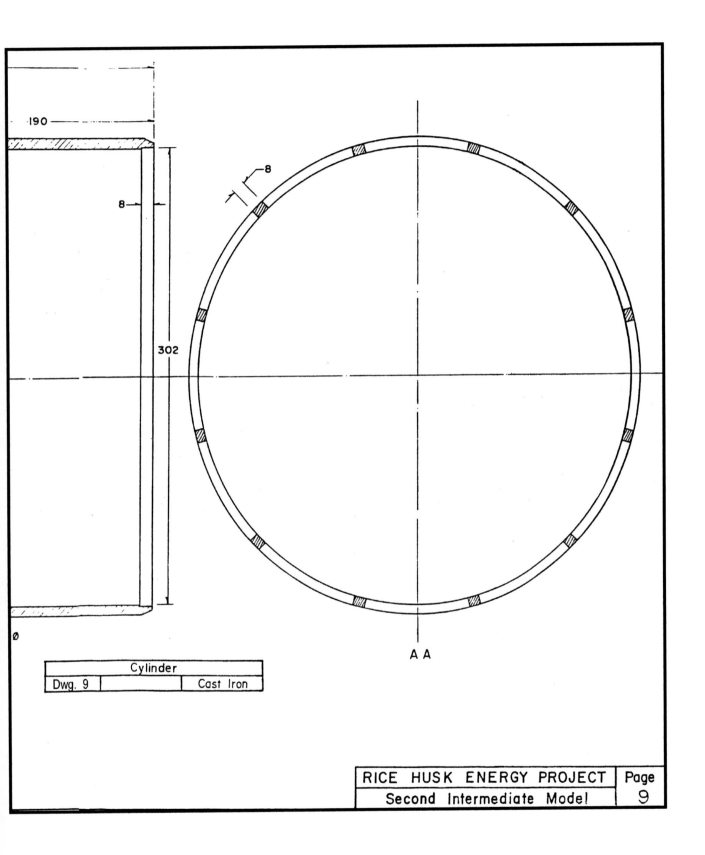

190	8	8	302	Ø

A A

Cylinder		
Dwg. 9		Cast Iron

RICE HUSK ENERGY PROJECT	Page
Second Intermediate Model	9

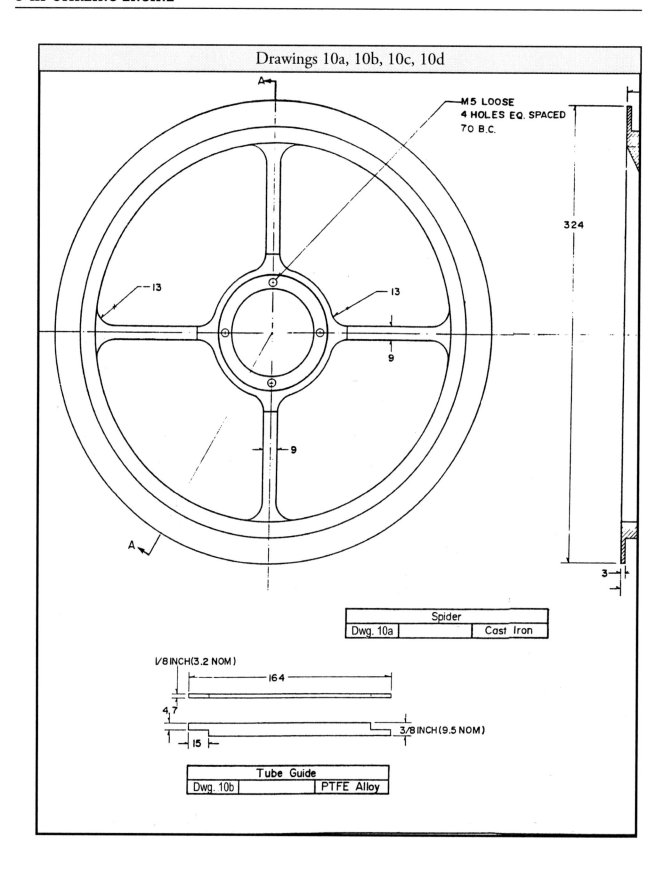

Drawings 10a, 10b, 10c, 10d

A

M5 LOOSE
4 HOLES EQ. SPACED
70 B.C.

324

13

13

9

9

3

A

Spider		
Dwg. 10a		Cast Iron

1/8 INCH (3.2 NOM)

164

4,7

15

3/8 INCH (9.5 NOM)

Tube Guide		
Dwg. 10b		PTFE Alloy

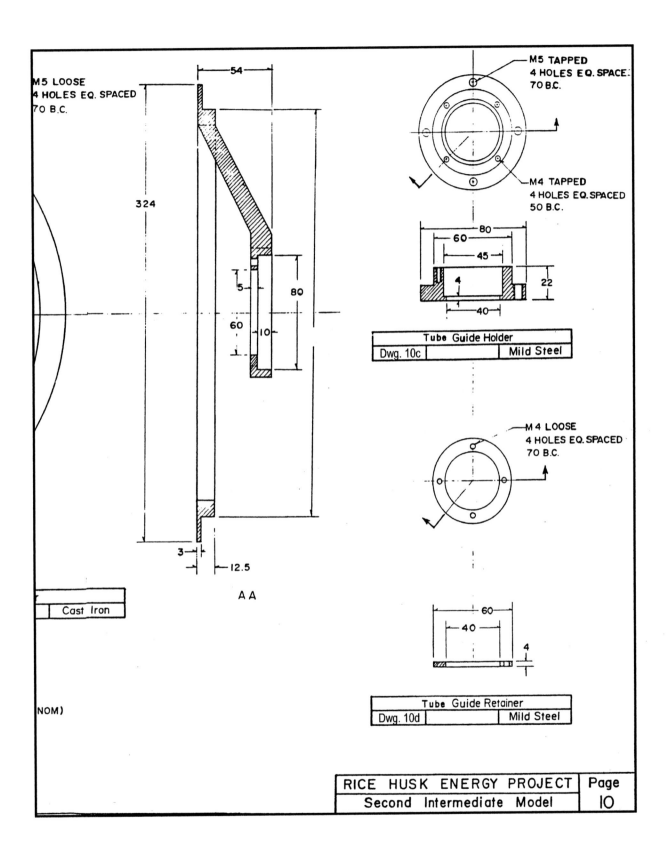

M5 LOOSE
4 HOLES EQ. SPACED
70 B.C.

54

324

5

80

60

10

3

12.5

A A

Cast Iron

NOM)

M5 TAPPED
4 HOLES EQ. SPACE.
70 B.C.

M4 TAPPED
4 HOLES EQ. SPACED
50 B.C.

80

60

45

4

22

40

Tube Guide Holder		
Dwg. 10c		Mild Steel

M 4 LOOSE
4 HOLES EQ. SPACED
70 B.C.

60

40

4

Tube Guide Retainer		
Dwg. 10d		Mild Steel

RICE HUSK ENERGY PROJECT	Page
Second Intermediate Model	10

153

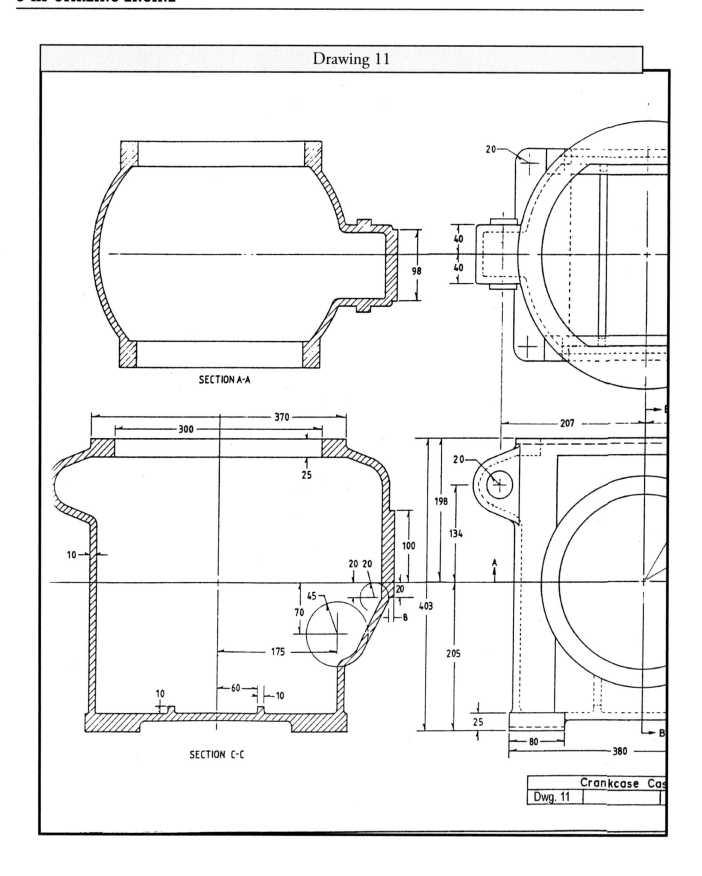

Drawing 11

SECTION A-A

SECTION C-C

Crankcase Cas

Dwg. 11

154

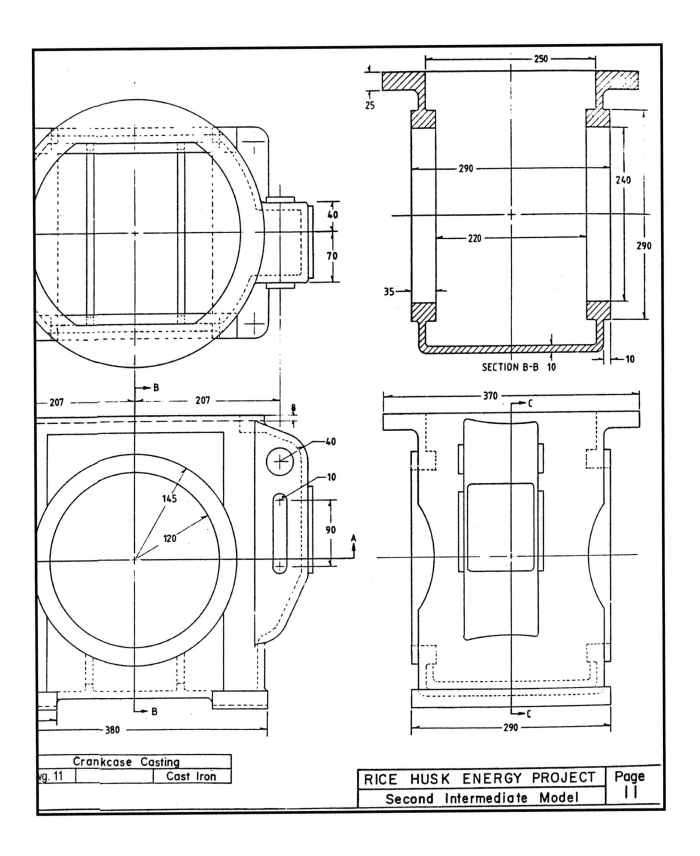

SECTION B-B 10

Crankcase Casting
Cast Iron
vg. 11

RICE HUSK ENERGY PROJECT
Second Intermediate Model

Page
11

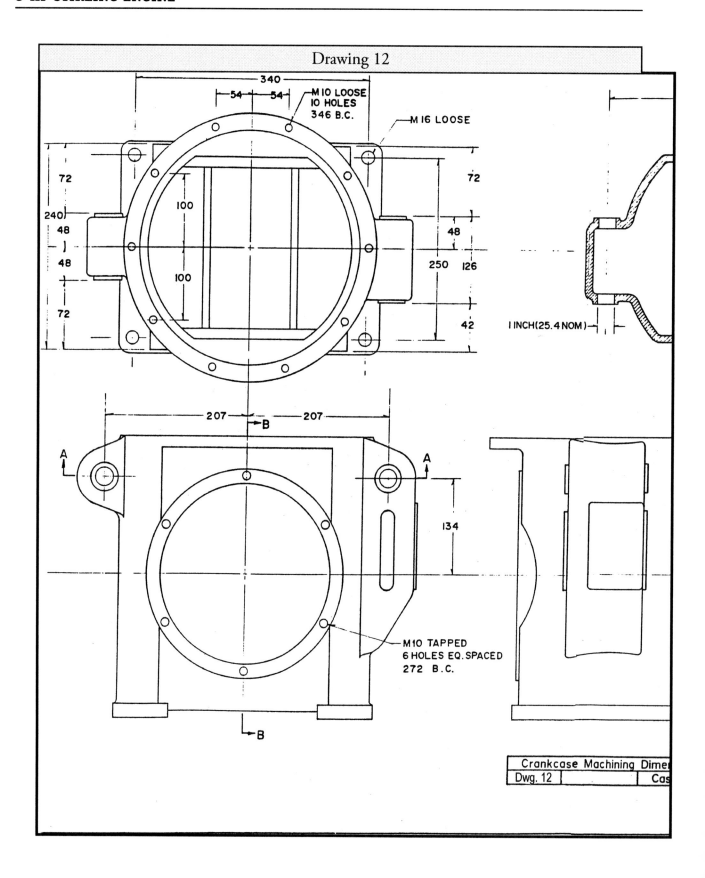

Drawing 12

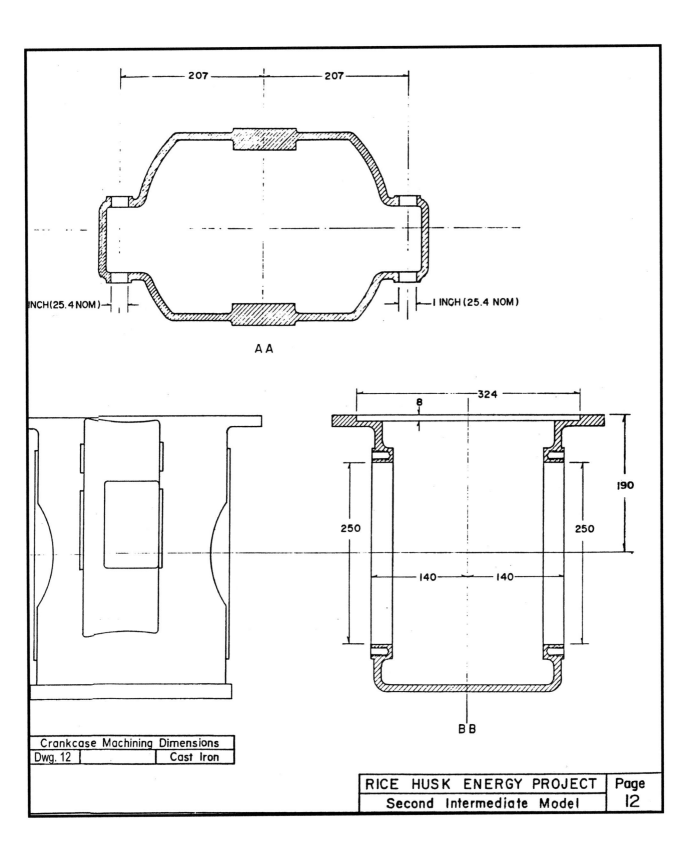

A A

I INCH(25.4 NOM) I INCH (25.4 NOM)

324
8
190
250 250
140 140

B B

Crankcase Machining Dimensions		
Dwg. 12		Cast Iron

RICE HUSK ENERGY PROJECT	Page
Second Intermediate Model	12

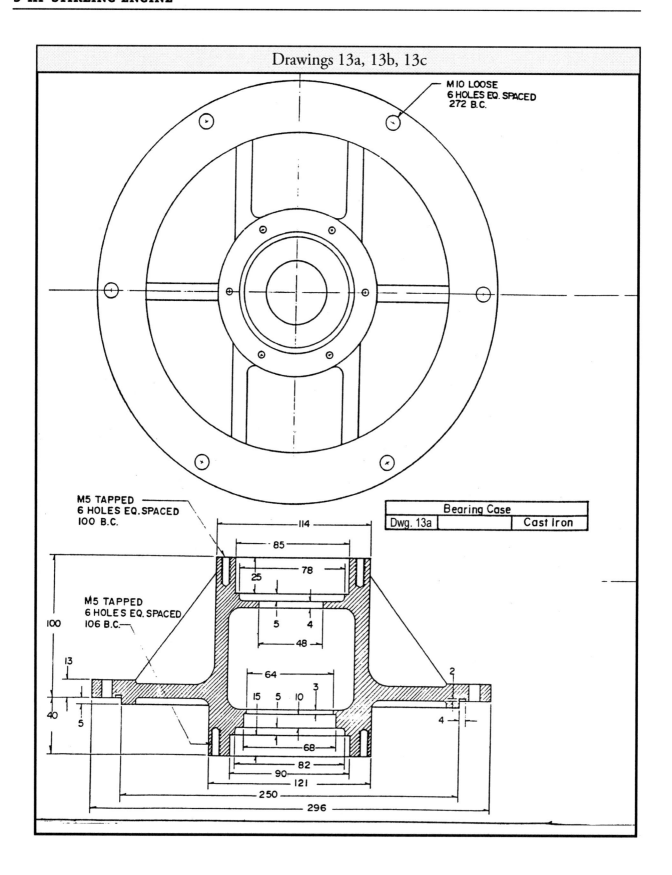

Drawings 13a, 13b, 13c

M IO LOOSE
6 HOLES EQ. SPACED
272 B.C.

M5 TAPPED
6 HOLES EQ. SPACED
100 B.C.

M5 TAPPED
6 HOLES EQ. SPACED
106 B.C.

Bearing Case		
Dwg. 13a		Cast Iron

114
85
78
25
5   4
48
64
3
15 5 10
2
13
100
40
5
68
82
90
121
4
250
296

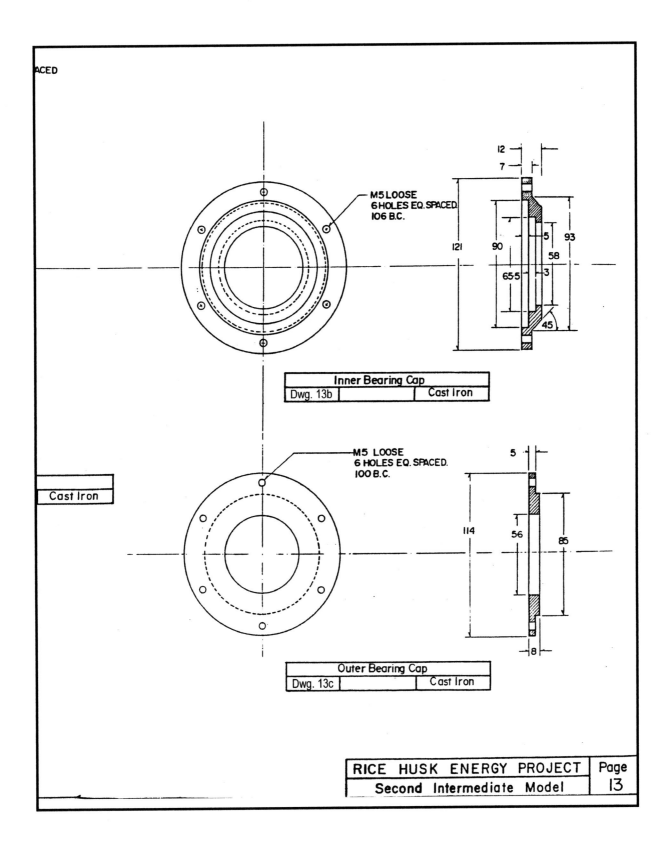

ACED

M5 LOOSE
6 HOLES EQ. SPACED.
106 B.C.

12
7
121
90
65.5
5
93
58
3
45

Inner Bearing Cap		
Dwg. 13b		Cast Iron

Cast Iron

M5 LOOSE
6 HOLES EQ. SPACED.
100 B.C.

5
114
56
85
8

Outer Bearing Cap		
Dwg. 13c		Cast Iron

RICE HUSK ENERGY PROJECT	Page
Second Intermediate Model	13

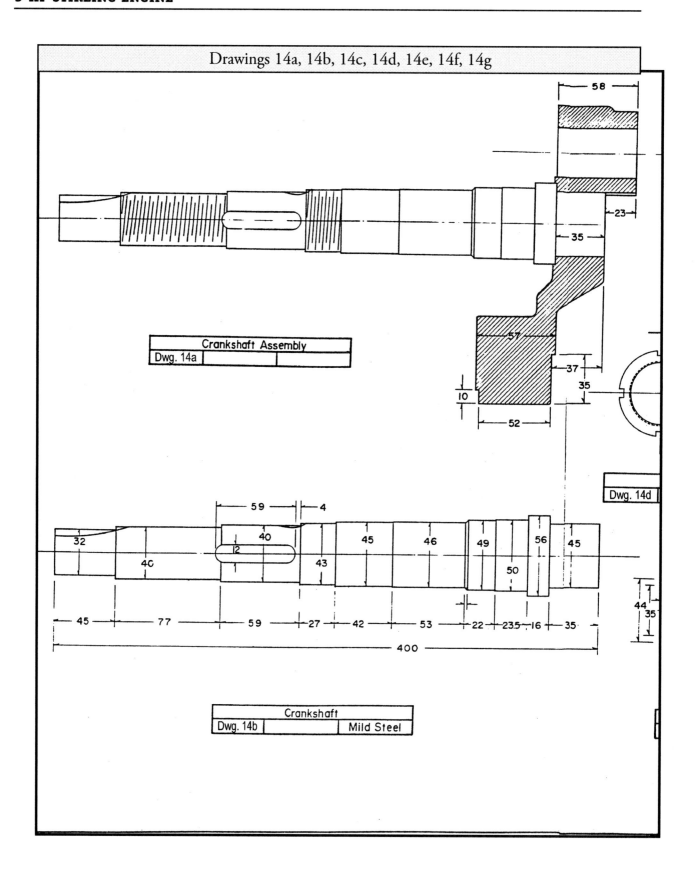

Drawings 14a, 14b, 14c, 14d, 14e, 14f, 14g

Crankshaft Assembly		
Dwg. 14a		

Dwg. 14d

Crankshaft		
Dwg. 14b		Mild Steel

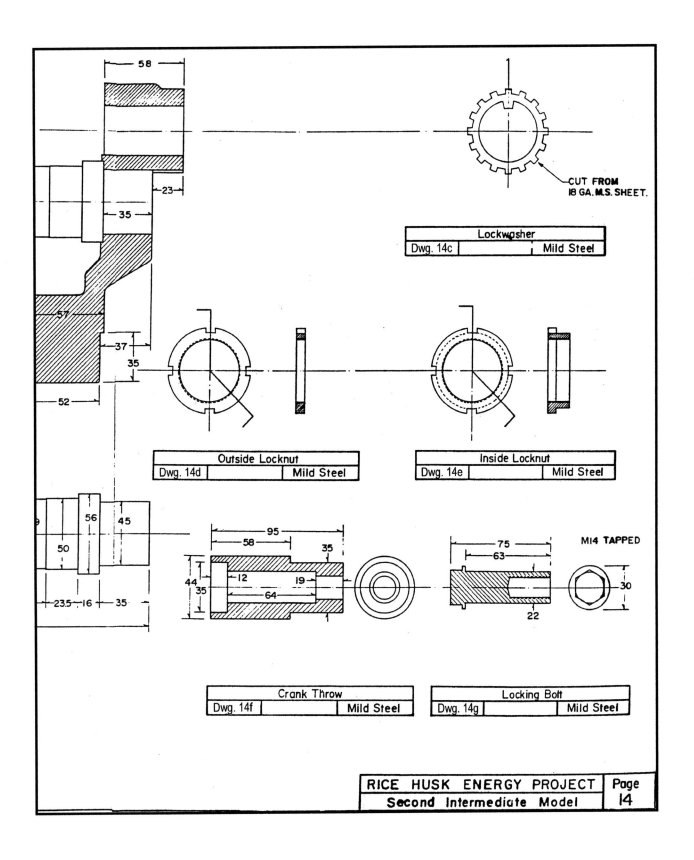

CUT FROM
18 GA. M.S. SHEET.

Lockwasher	
Dwg. 14c	Mild Steel

Outside Locknut	
Dwg. 14d	Mild Steel

Inside Locknut	
Dwg. 14e	Mild Steel

M14 TAPPED

Crank Throw	
Dwg. 14f	Mild Steel

Locking Bolt	
Dwg. 14g	Mild Steel

RICE HUSK ENERGY PROJECT	Page
Second Intermediate Model	14

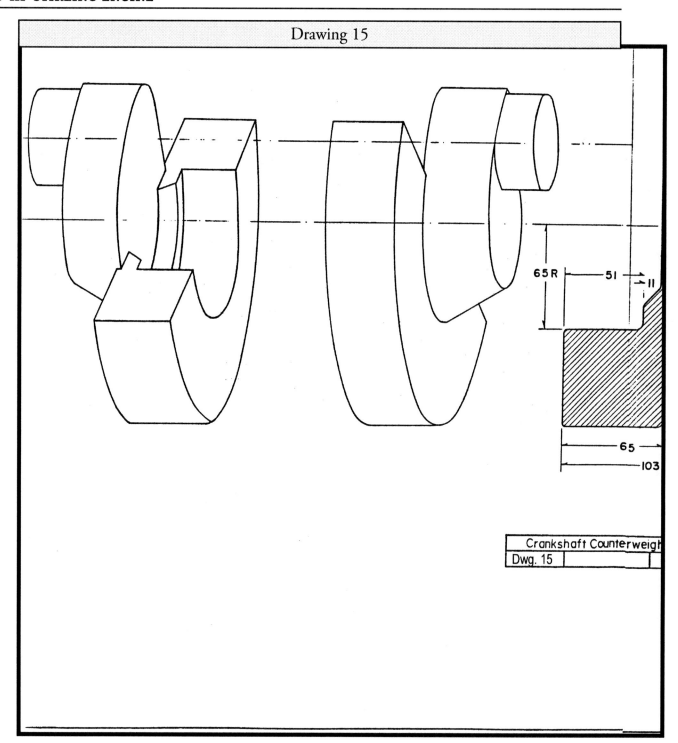

Drawing 15

65 R 51 11

65

103

Crankshaft Counterweight

Dwg. 15

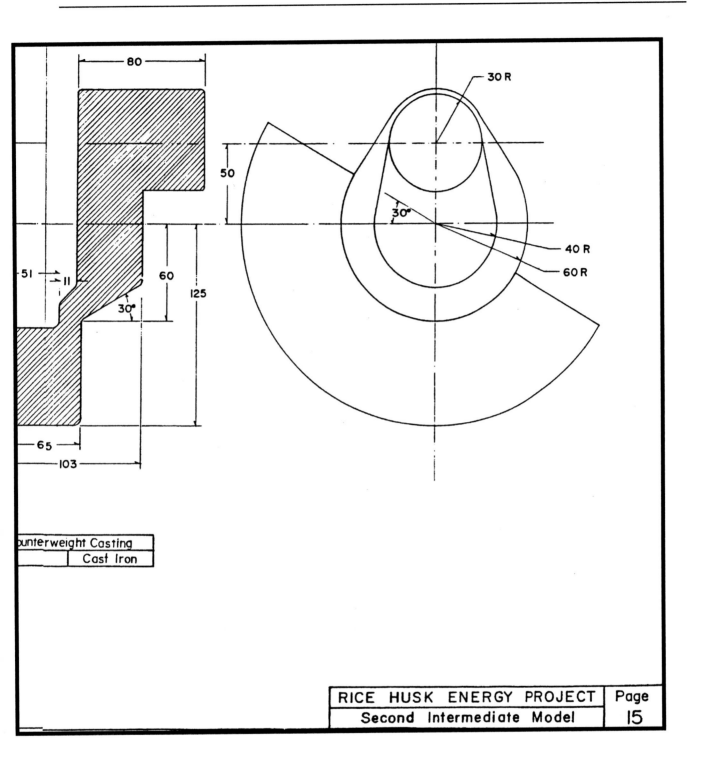

RICE HUSK ENERGY PROJECT	Page
Second Intermediate Model	15

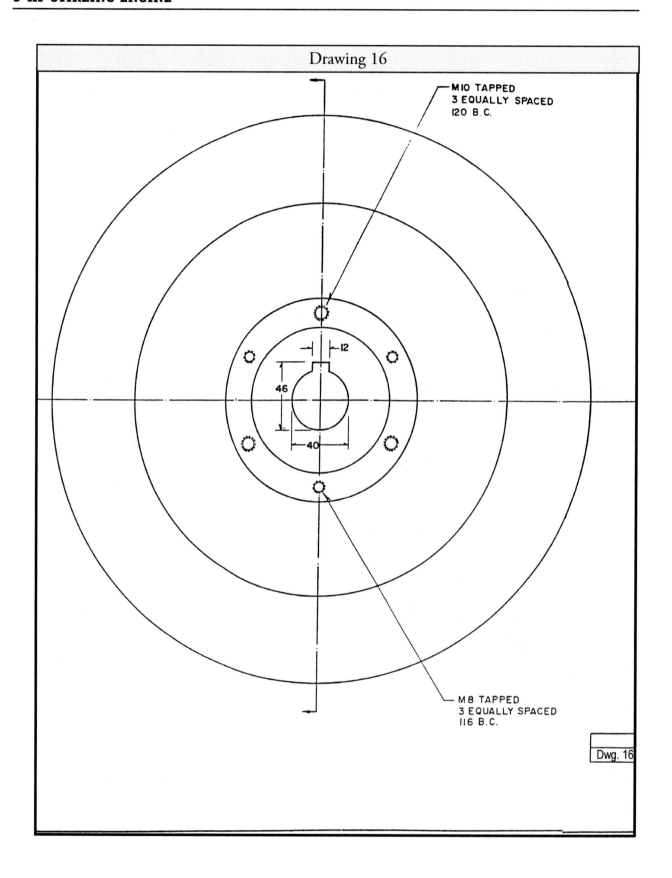

Drawing 16

MIO TAPPED
3 EQUALLY SPACED
I2O B.C.

I2

46

40

M8 TAPPED
3 EQUALLY SPACED
II6 B.C.

Dwg. 16

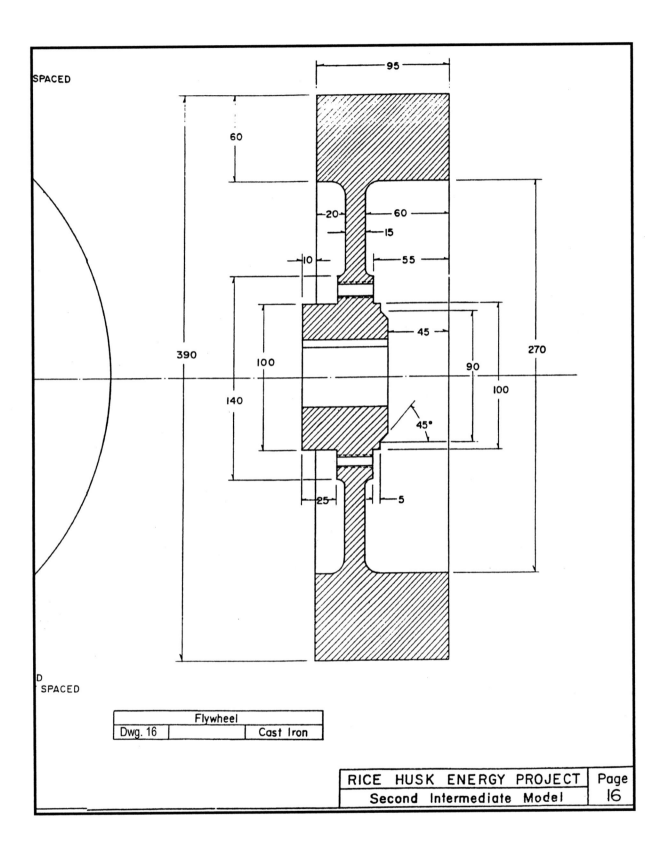

SPACED

390

60

95

20

60

15

10

55

45

100

140

90

270

100

45°

25

5

D
SPACED

Flywheel		
Dwg. 16		Cast Iron

RICE HUSK ENERGY PROJECT	Page
Second Intermediate Model	16

Drawings 17a, 17b, 17c

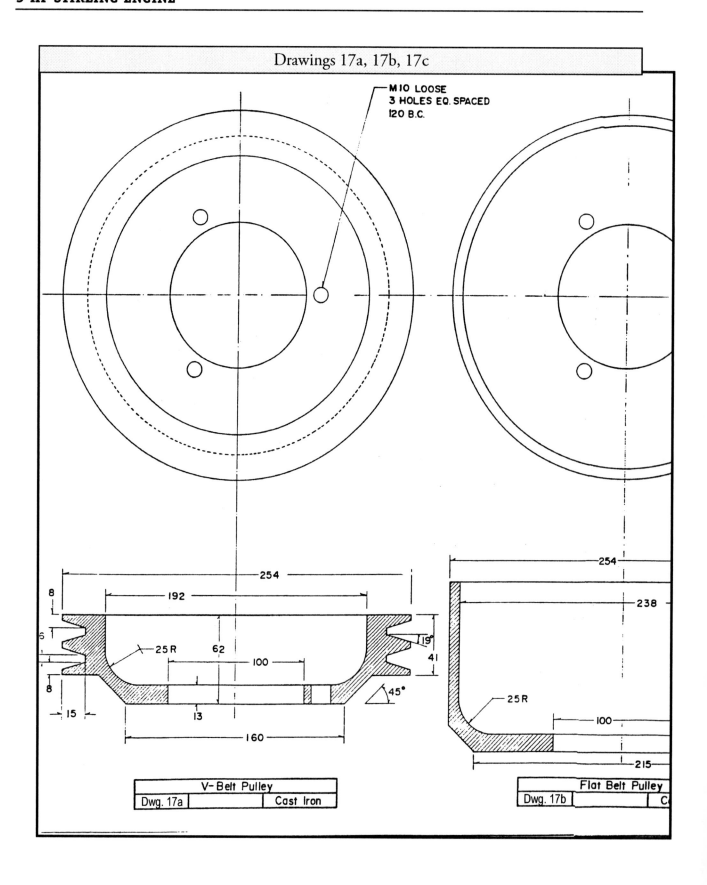

M10 LOOSE
3 HOLES EQ. SPACED
120 B.C.

254
192
8
6
25 R
62
100
45°
8
15
13
160

19°
41

	V-Belt Pulley	
Dwg. 17a		Cast Iron

254
238
25 R
100
215

Flat Belt Pulley	
Dwg. 17b	C

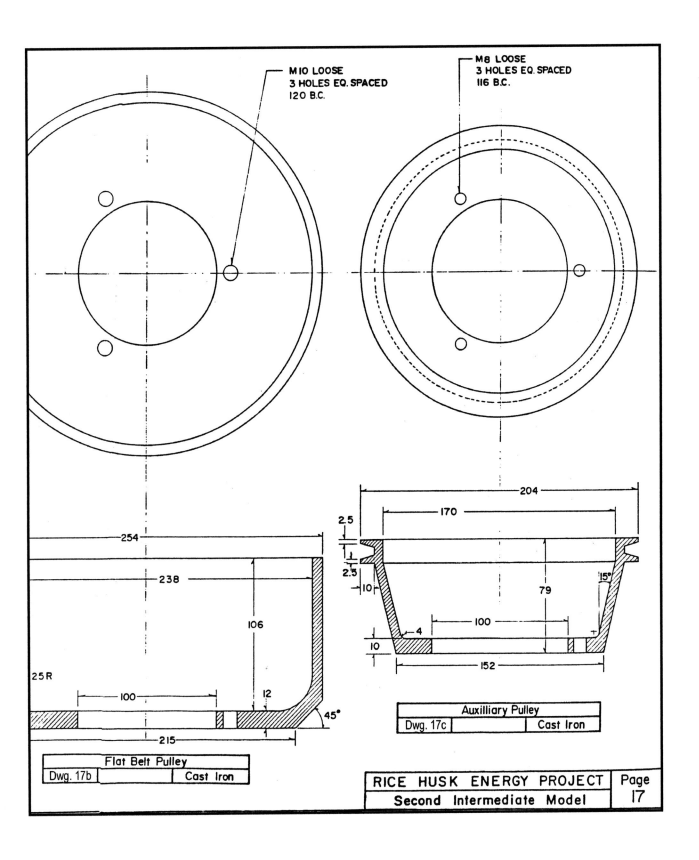

M10 LOOSE
3 HOLES EQ. SPACED
120 B.C.

M8 LOOSE
3 HOLES EQ. SPACED
116 B.C.

254

238

106

25R

100

12

215

45°

Flat Belt Pulley		
Dwg. 17b		Cast Iron

204

170

2.5

2.5

10

79

15°

100

4

10

152

Auxilliary Pulley		
Dwg. 17c		Cast Iron

RICE HUSK ENERGY PROJECT	Page
Second Intermediate Model	17

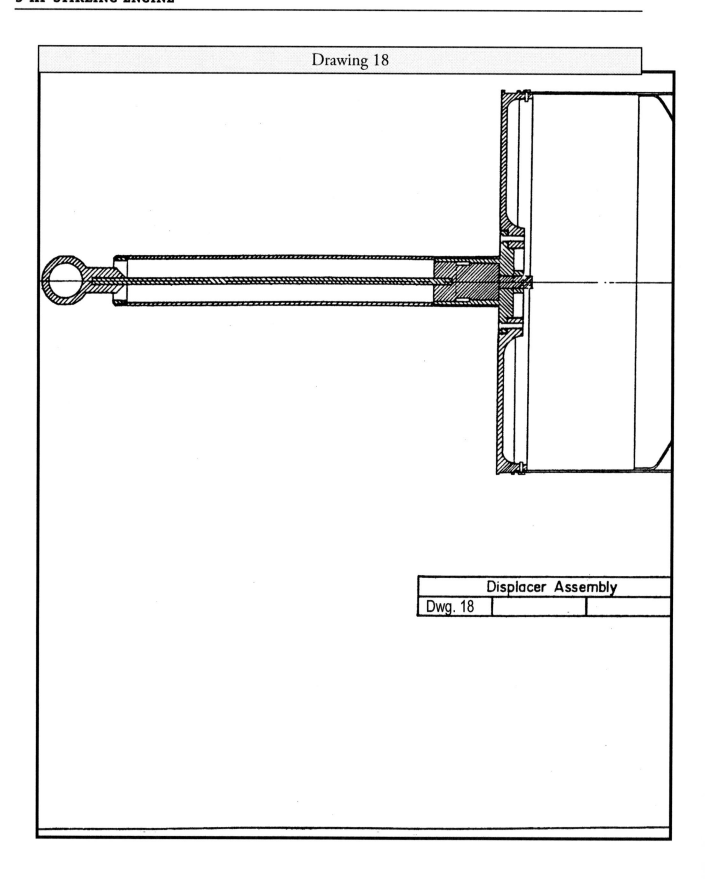

Drawing 18

Displacer Assembly

Dwg. 18

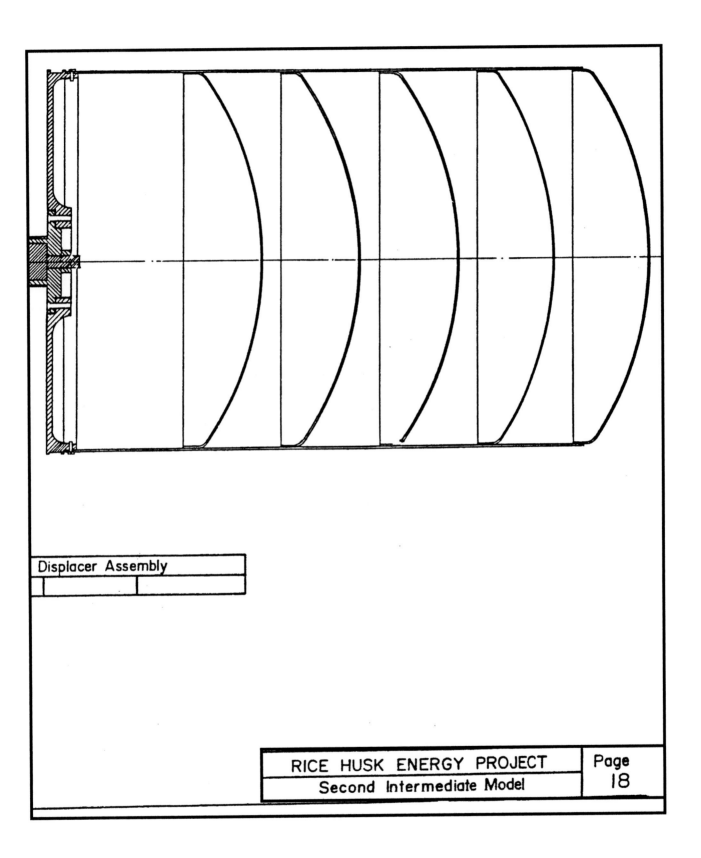

Displacer Assembly

RICE HUSK ENERGY PROJECT
Second Intermediate Model

Page
18

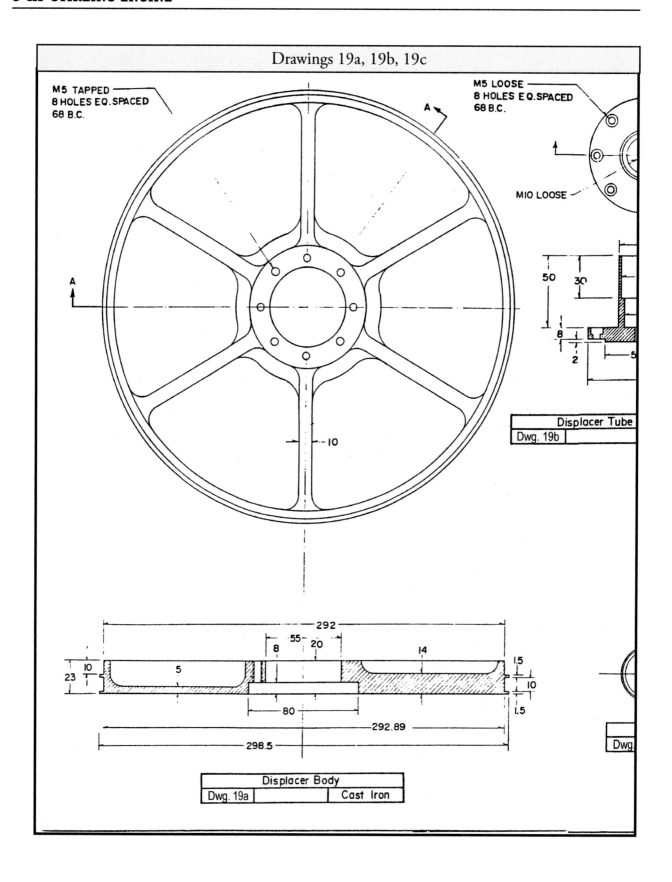

Drawings 19a, 19b, 19c

M5 TAPPED
8 HOLES EQ. SPACED
68 B.C.

M5 LOOSE
8 HOLES EQ. SPACED
68 B.C.

MIO LOOSE

Displacer Tube

Dwg. 19b

Displacer Body

Dwg. 19a   Cast Iron

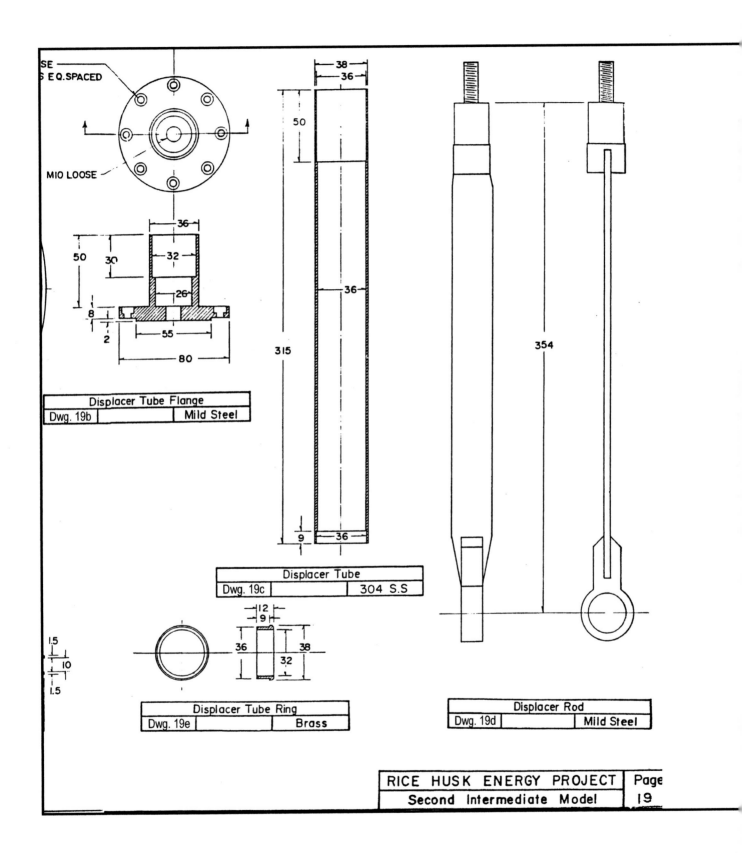

SE
6 EQ.SPACED

MIO LOOSE

Displacer Tube Flange	
Dwg. 19b	Mild Steel

Displacer Tube	
Dwg. 19c	304 S.S

Displacer Tube Ring	
Dwg. 19e	Brass

Displacer Rod	
Dwg. 19d	Mild Steel

RICE HUSK ENERGY PROJECT	Page
Second Intermediate Model	19

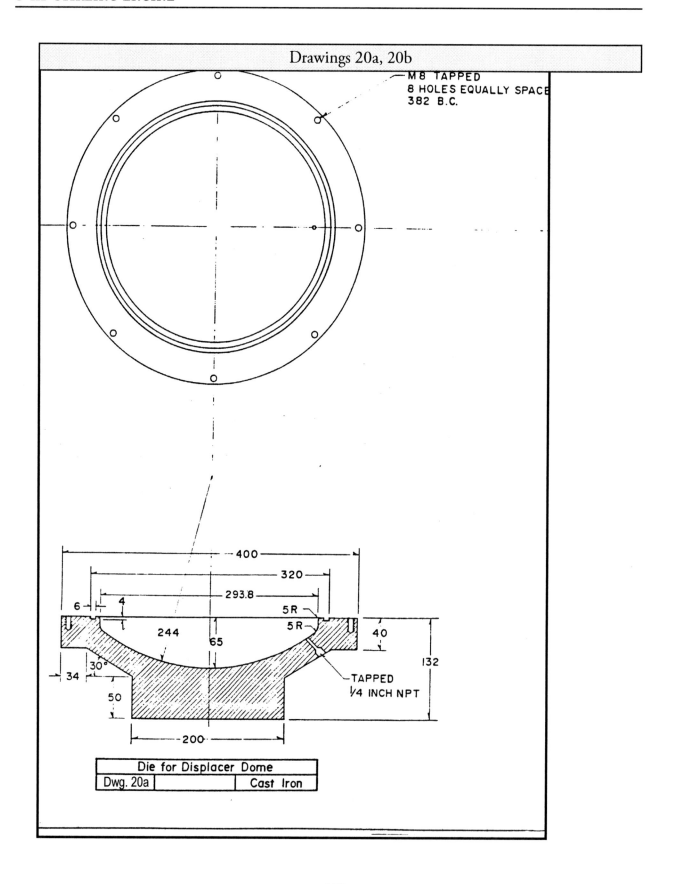

Drawings 20a, 20b

M8 TAPPED
8 HOLES EQUALLY SPACE
382 B.C.

400

320

293.8

6 4

5R

5R

244

65

40

132

30°

TAPPED
1/4 INCH NPT

34

50

200

Die for Displacer Dome		
Dwg. 20a		Cast Iron

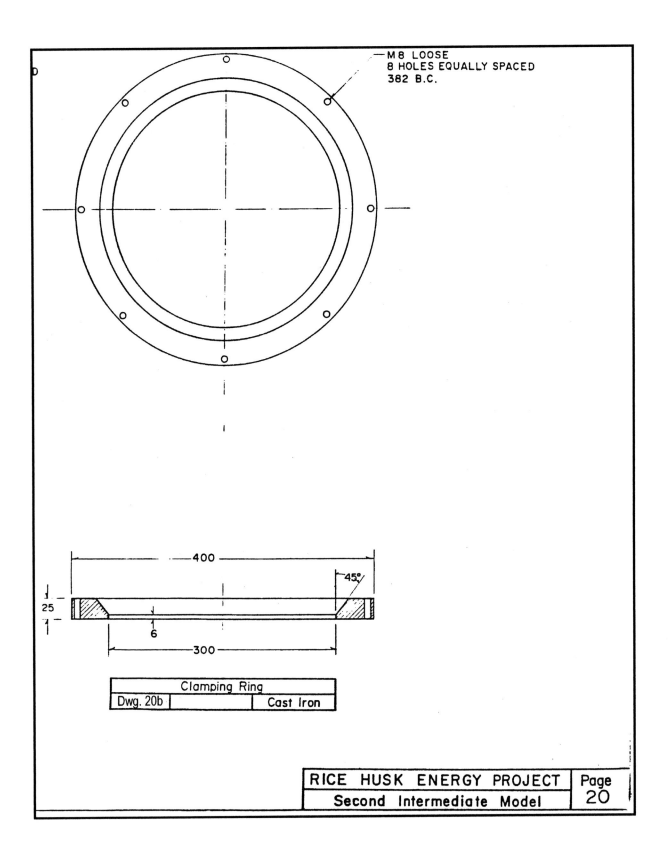

M8 LOOSE
8 HOLES EQUALLY SPACED
382 B.C.

400

45°

25

6

300

Clamping Ring		
Dwg. 20b		Cast Iron

RICE HUSK ENERGY PROJECT	Page
Second Intermediate Model	20

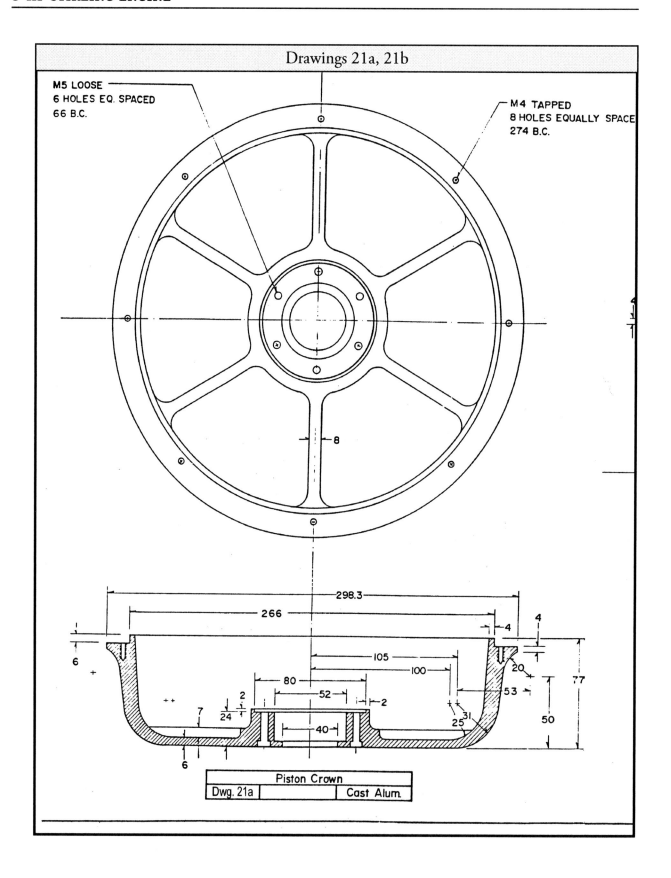

Drawings 21a, 21b

M5 LOOSE
6 HOLES EQ. SPACED
66 B.C.

M4 TAPPED
8 HOLES EQUALLY SPACE
274 B.C.

Piston Crown

| Dwg. 21a | | Cast Alum. |

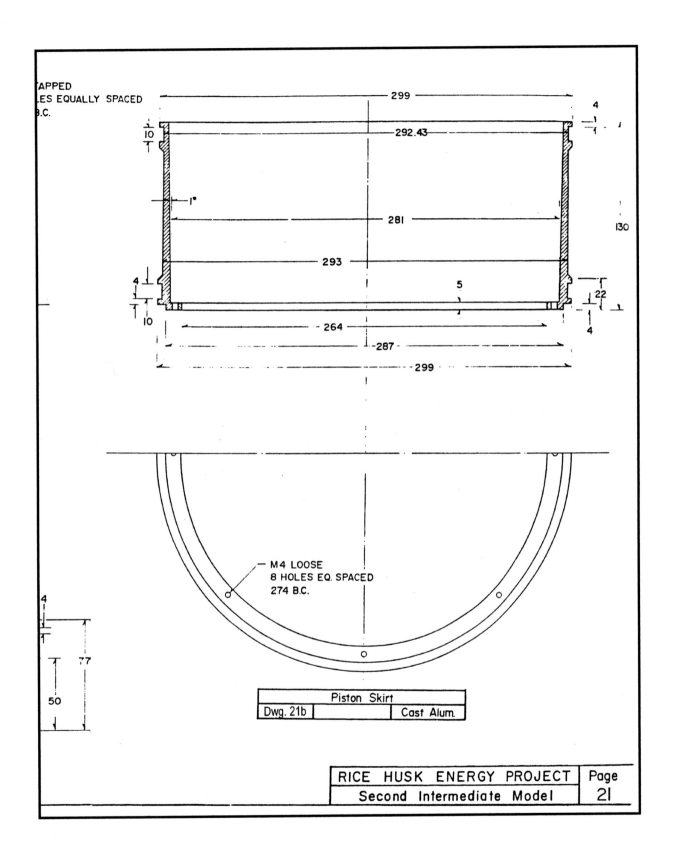

TAPPED
LES EQUALLY SPACED
B.C.

299

292.43

10

4

1°

281

130

293

4

5

10

22

4

264

-287-

299

M4 LOOSE
8 HOLES EQ. SPACED
274 B.C.

4

77

50

Piston Skirt		
Dwg. 21b		Cast Alum.

RICE HUSK ENERGY PROJECT	Page
Second Intermediate Model	21

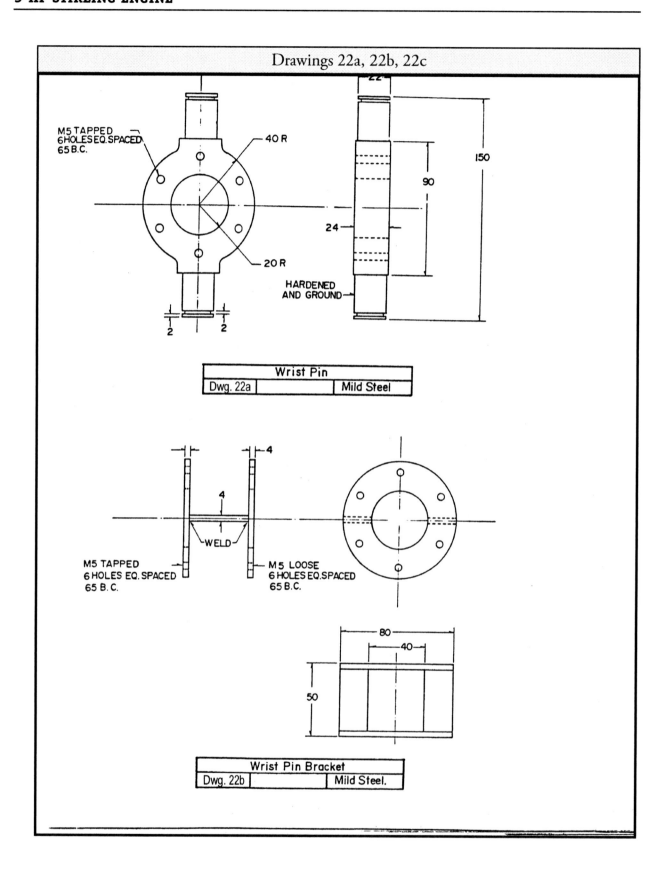

Wrist Pin		
Dwg. 22a		Mild Steel

Wrist Pin Bracket		
Dwg. 22b		Mild Steel.

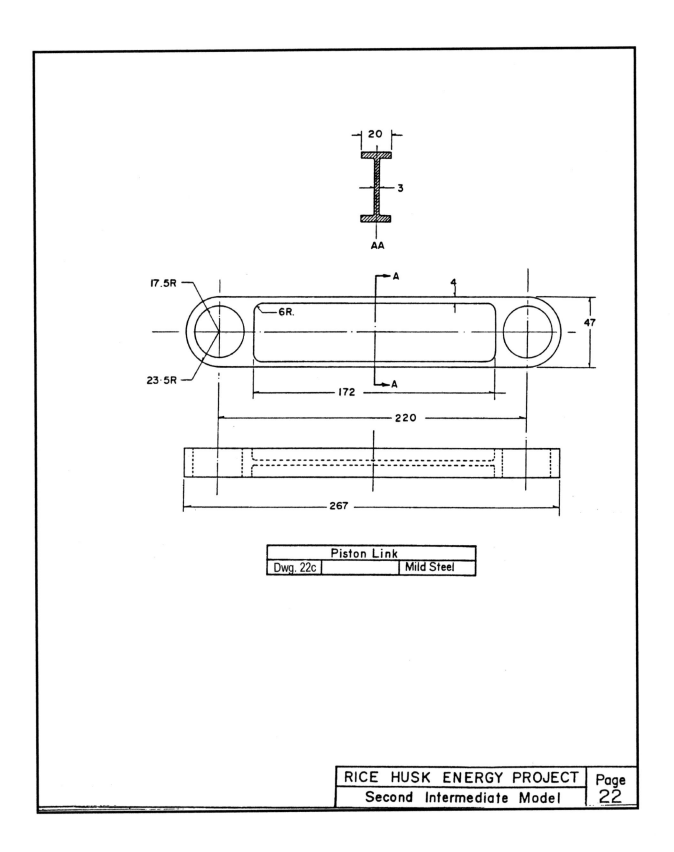

Piston Link		
Dwg. 22c		Mild Steel

RICE HUSK ENERGY PROJECT	Page
Second Intermediate Model	22

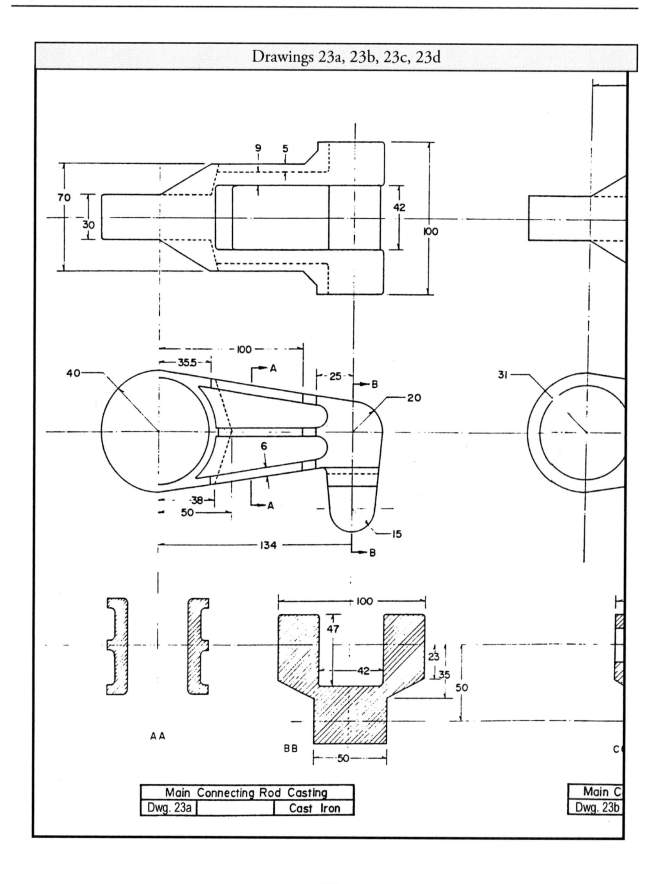

Drawings 23a, 23b, 23c, 23d

Main Connecting Rod Casting		
Dwg. 23a		Cast Iron

Main C
Dwg. 23b

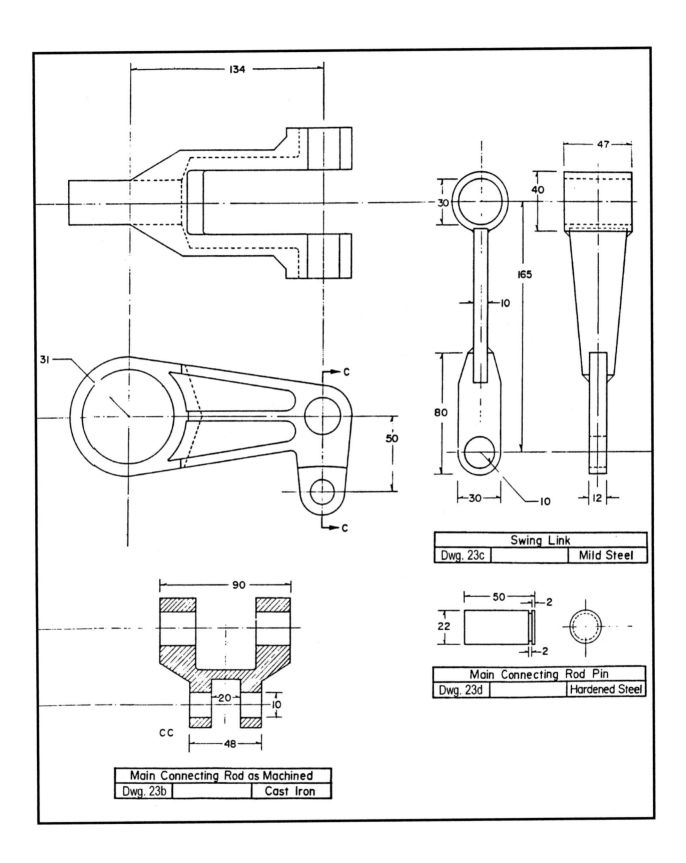

Swing Link

Dwg. 23c		Mild Steel

Main Connecting Rod Pin

Dwg. 23d		Hardened Steel

Main Connecting Rod as Machined

Dwg. 23b		Cast Iron

179

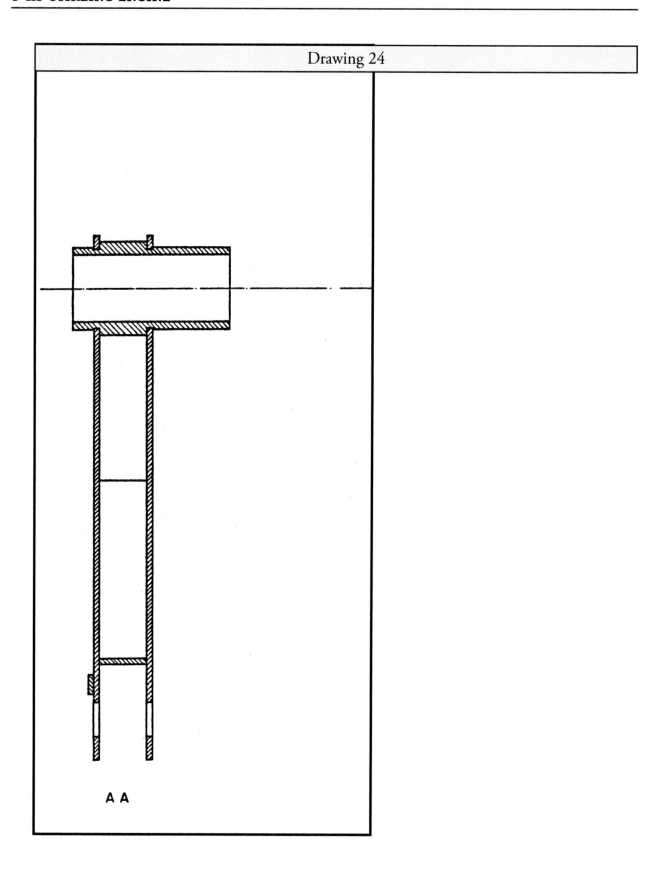

Drawing 24

A A

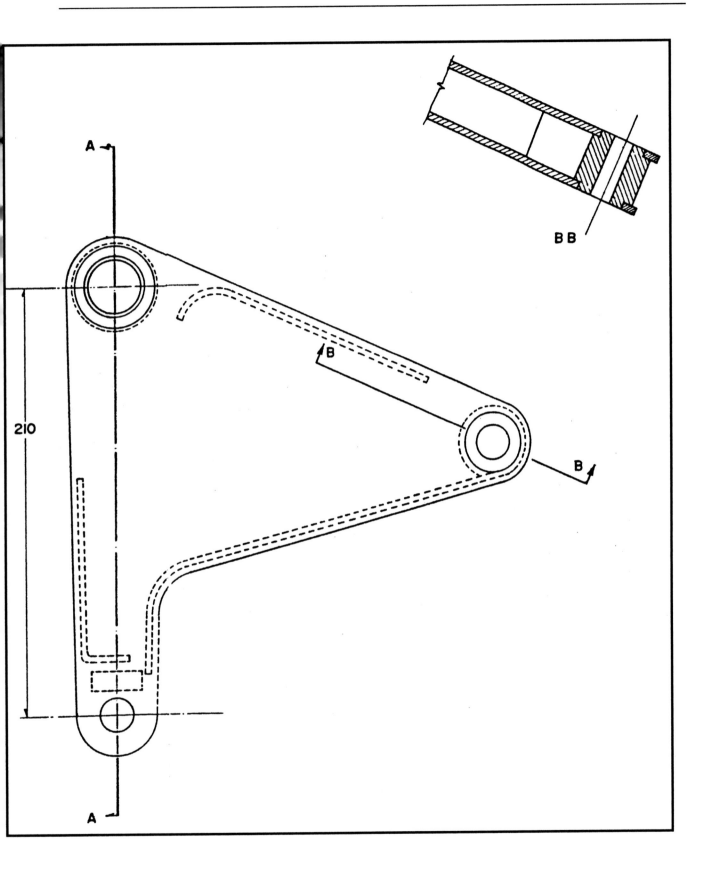

Drawings 25a, 25b, 25c, 25d, 25e

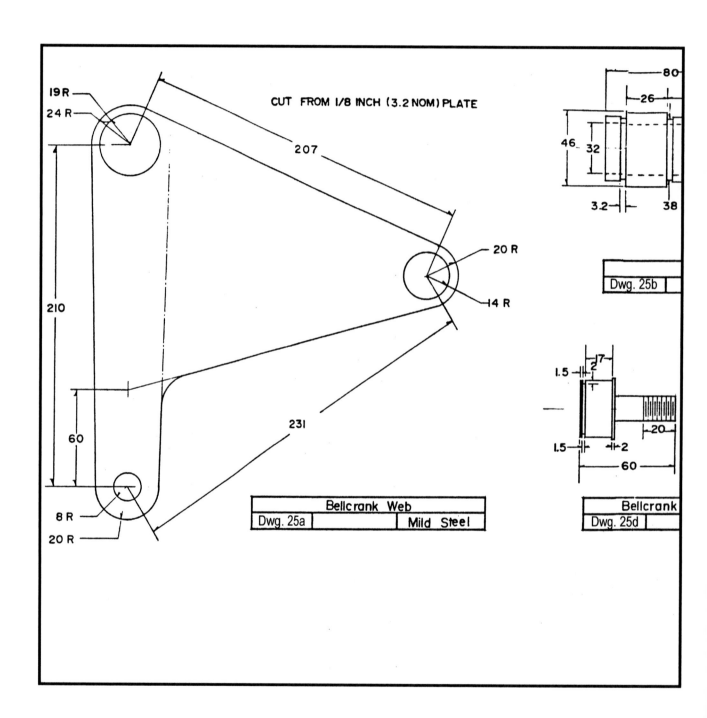

CUT FROM 1/8 INCH (3.2 NOM) PLATE

19 R
24 R
207
210
20 R
14 R
60
231
8 R
20 R

80
26
46
32
3.2
38

Dwg. 25b

1.5
7
2
1.5
2
20
60

Bellcrank Web		
Dwg. 25a		Mild Steel

Bellcrank	
Dwg. 25d	

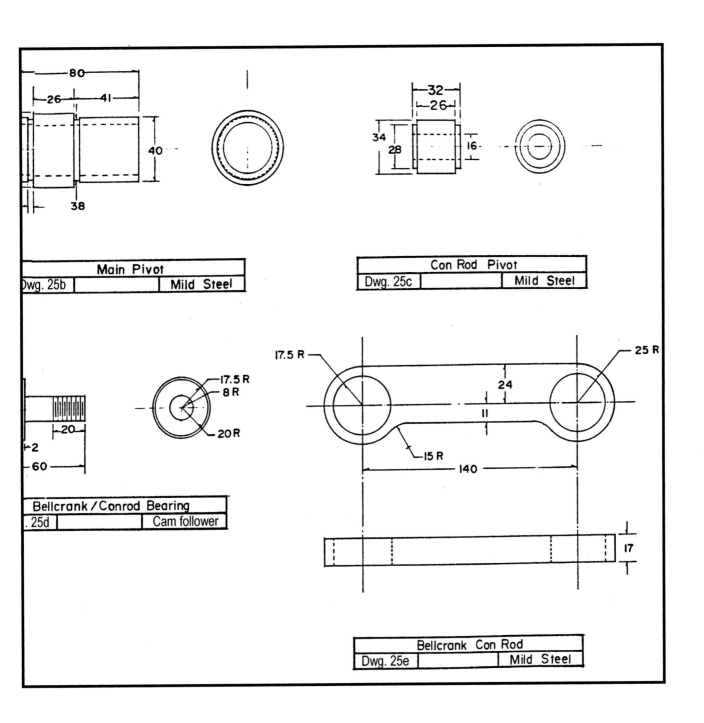

Main Pivot		
Dwg. 25b		Mild Steel

Con Rod Pivot		
Dwg. 25c		Mild Steel

Bellcrank / Conrod Bearing		
.25d		Cam follower

Bellcrank Con Rod		
Dwg. 25e		Mild Steel

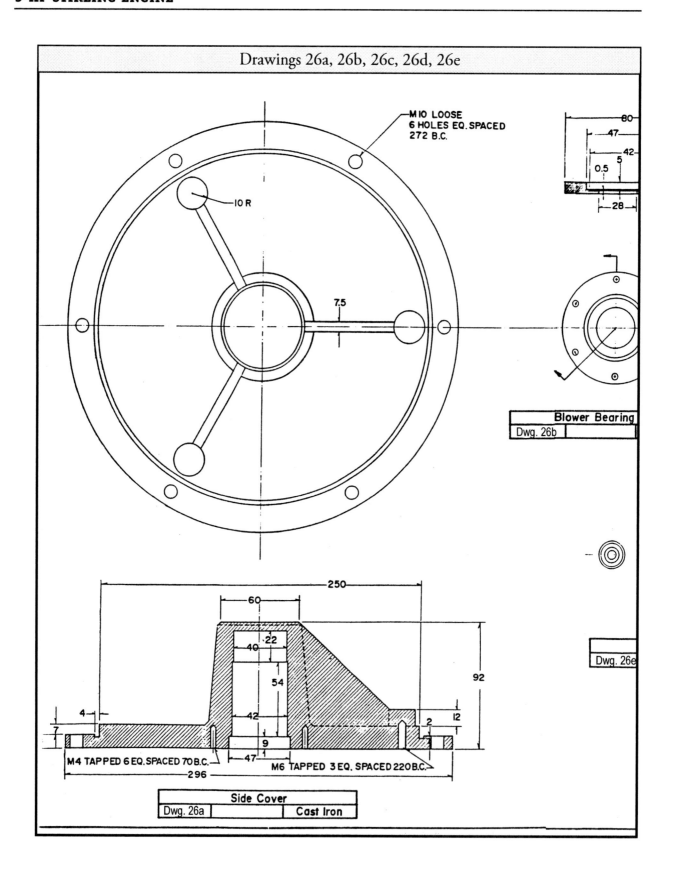

Drawings 26a, 26b, 26c, 26d, 26e

M10 LOOSE
6 HOLES EQ. SPACED
272 B.C.

10 R

7,5

80
47
42
5
0.5
28

Blower Bearing
Dwg. 26b

Dwg. 26e

250
60
22
40
54
42
9
47
4
7
92
12
2
296

M4 TAPPED 6 EQ. SPACED 70 B.C.
M6 TAPPED 3 EQ. SPACED 220 B.C.

Side Cover
Dwg. 26a | Cast Iron

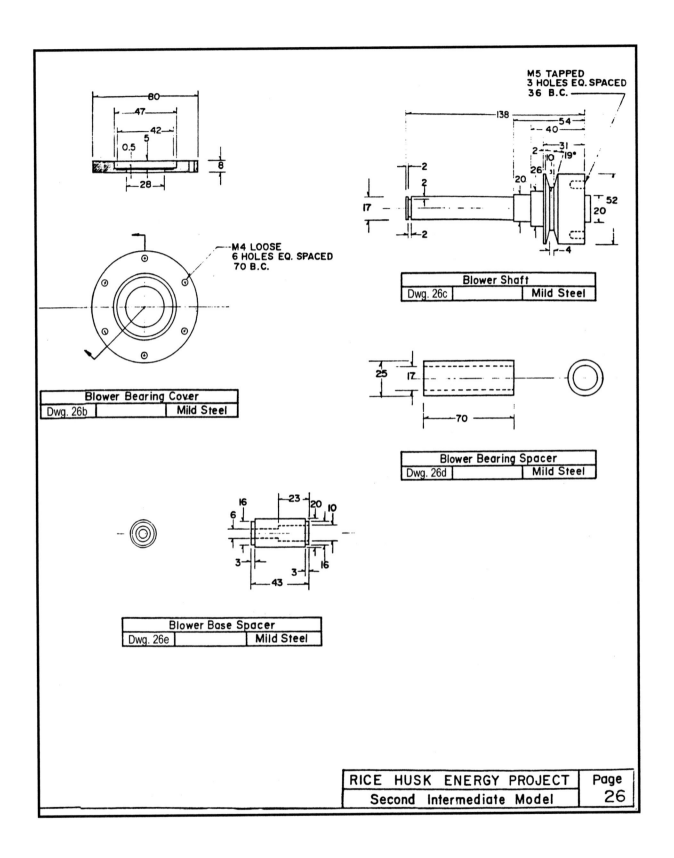

Blower Bearing Cover
Dwg. 26b		Mild Steel

Blower Shaft
Dwg. 26c		Mild Steel

Blower Bearing Spacer
Dwg. 26d		Mild Steel

Blower Base Spacer
Dwg. 26e		Mild Steel

RICE HUSK ENERGY PROJECT	Page
Second Intermediate Model	26

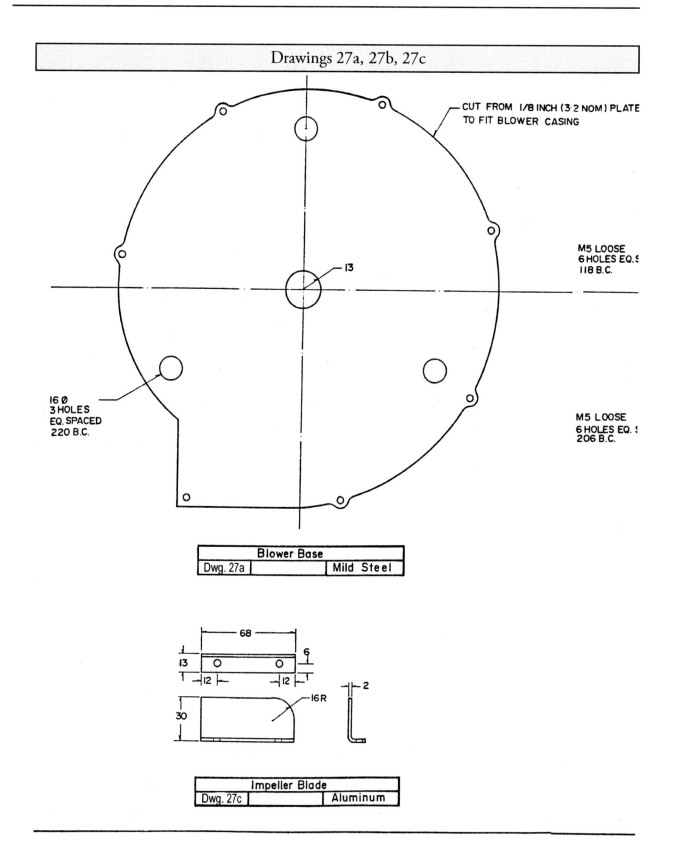

Drawings 27a, 27b, 27c

CUT FROM 1/8 INCH (3·2 NOM) PLATE TO FIT BLOWER CASING

13

M5 LOOSE
6 HOLES EQ. S
118 B.C.

16 Ø
3 HOLES
EQ. SPACED
220 B.C.

M5 LOOSE
6 HOLES EQ. S
206 B.C.

Blower Base		
Dwg. 27a		Mild Steel

68
6
13
12
12
16R
30
2

Impeller Blade		
Dwg. 27c		Aluminum

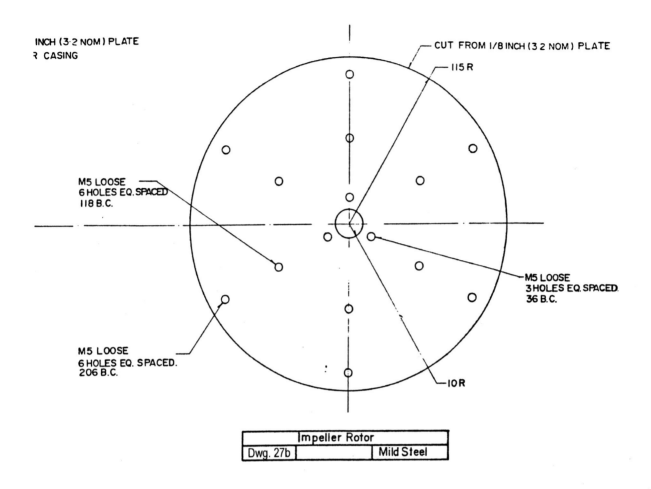

INCH (3·2 NOM) PLATE
R CASING

CUT FROM 1/8 INCH (3·2 NOM) PLATE

115 R

M5 LOOSE
6 HOLES EQ. SPACED
118 B.C.

M5 LOOSE
3 HOLES EQ. SPACED.
36 B.C.

M5 LOOSE
6 HOLES EQ. SPACED.
206 B.C.

10 R

Impeller Rotor		
Dwg. 27b		Mild Steel

RICE HUSK ENERGY PROJECT	Page
Second Intermediate Model	27

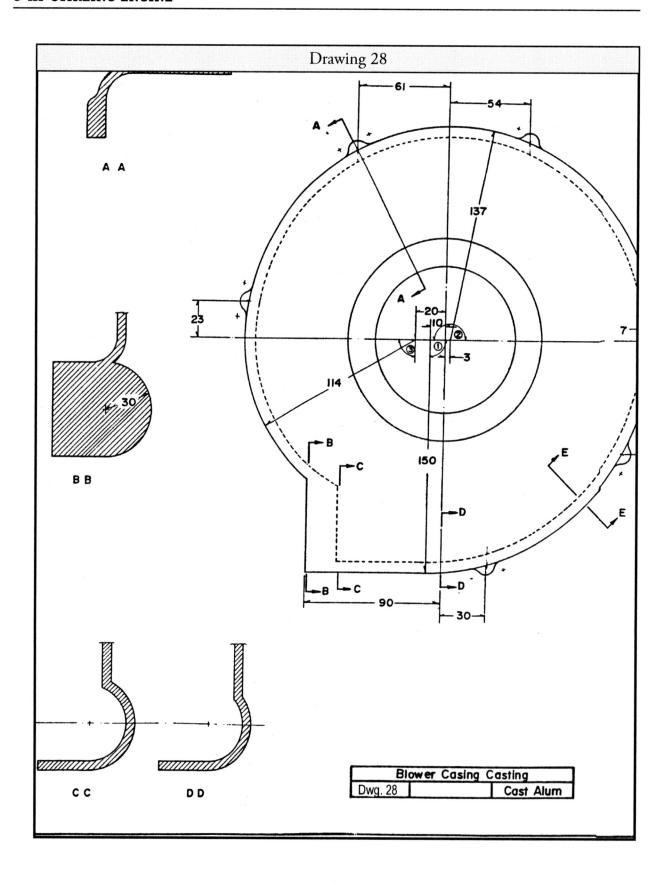

Drawing 28

Blower Casing Casting		
Dwg. 28		Cast Alum

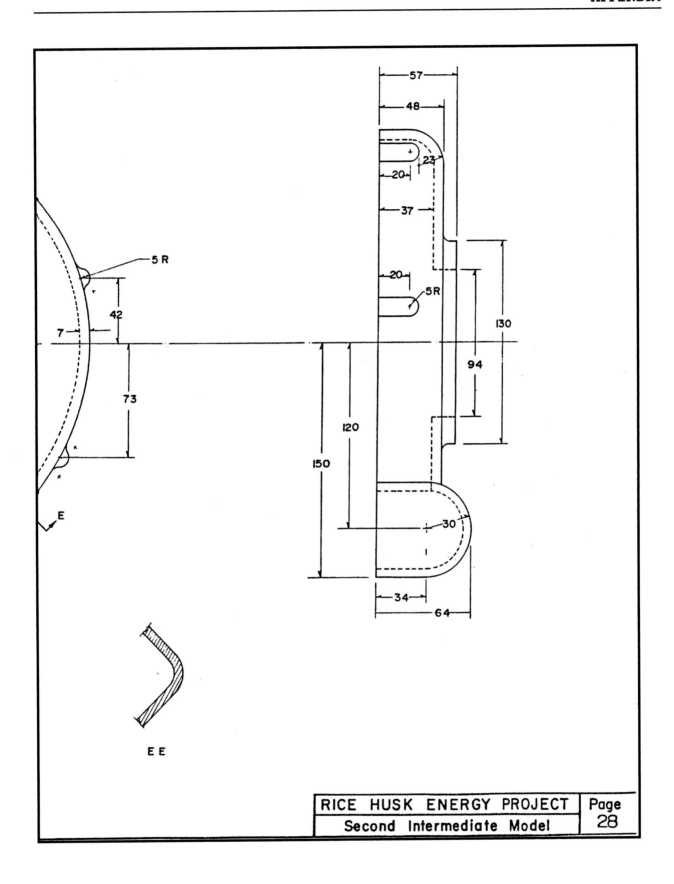

57

48

5 R

23

20

42

37

7

20

5R

130

73

94

120

150

30

E

34

64

E E

RICE HUSK ENERGY PROJECT | Page
Second Intermediate Model | 28

Drawings 29a, 29b

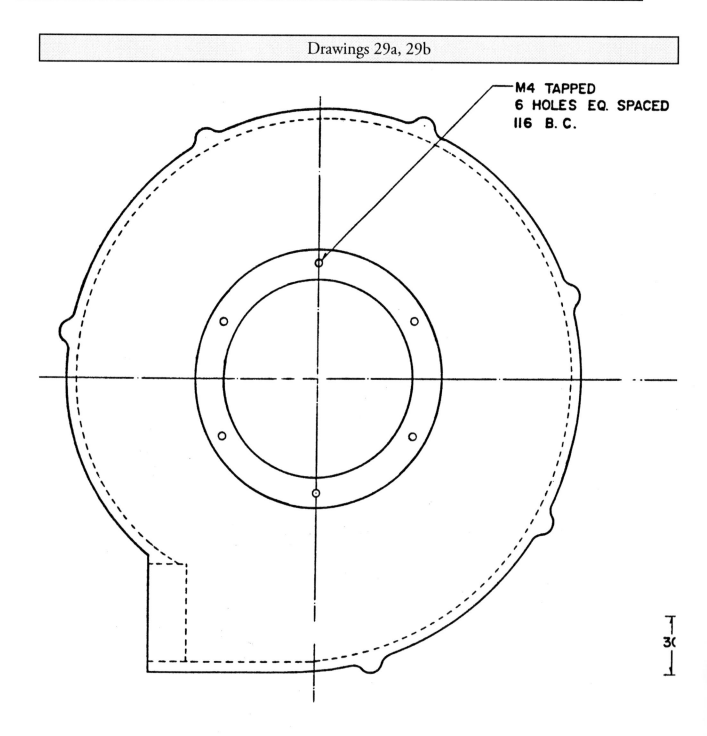

M4 TAPPED
6 HOLES EQ. SPACED
116 B. C.

Blower Casing Finishing Dimensions		
Dwg. 29a		Cast Alum.

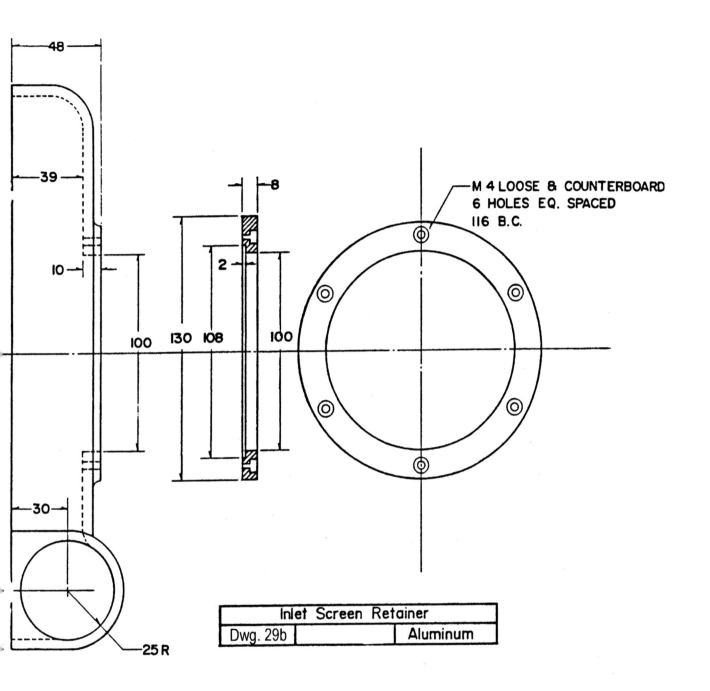

Inlet Screen Retainer		
Dwg. 29b		Aluminum

Drawings 30a, 30b, 30c, 30d

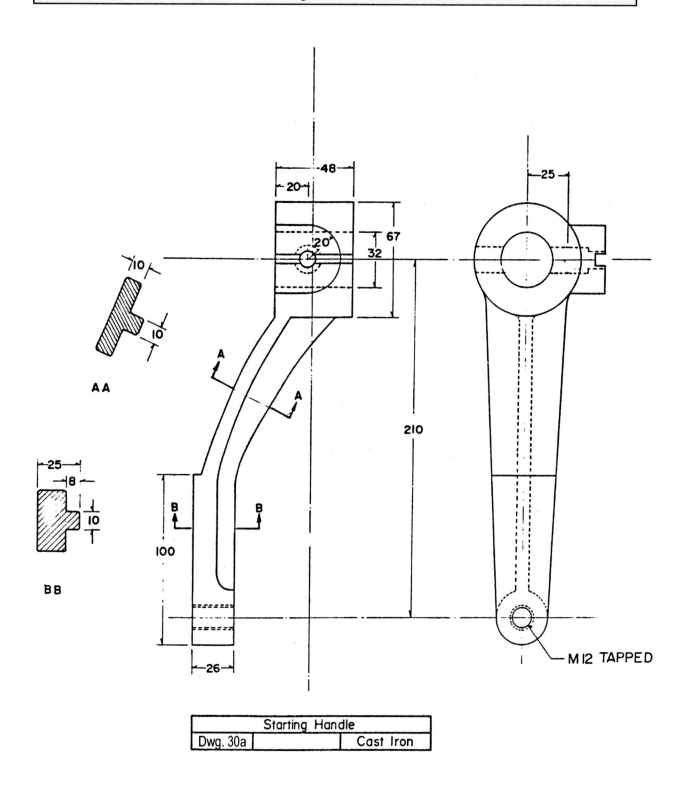

AA

BB

Starting Handle		
Dwg. 30a		Cast Iron

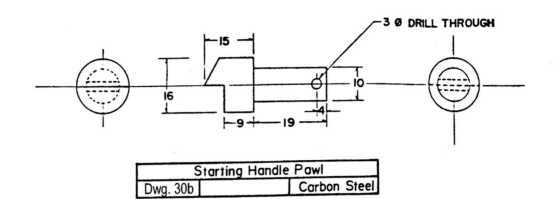

3 Ø DRILL THROUGH

Starting Handle Pawl		
Dwg. 30b		Carbon Steel

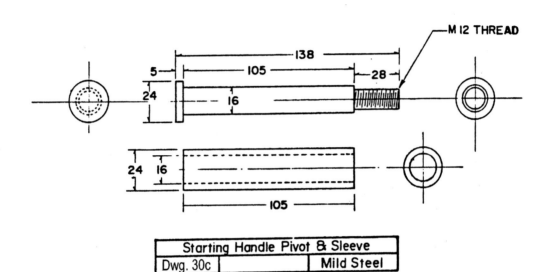

M 12 THREAD

Starting Handle Pivot & Sleeve		
Dwg. 30c		Mild Steel

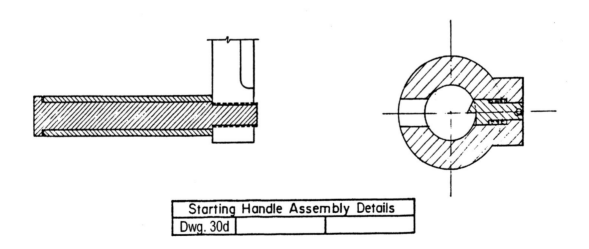

Starting Handle Assembly Details		
Dwg. 30d		

193

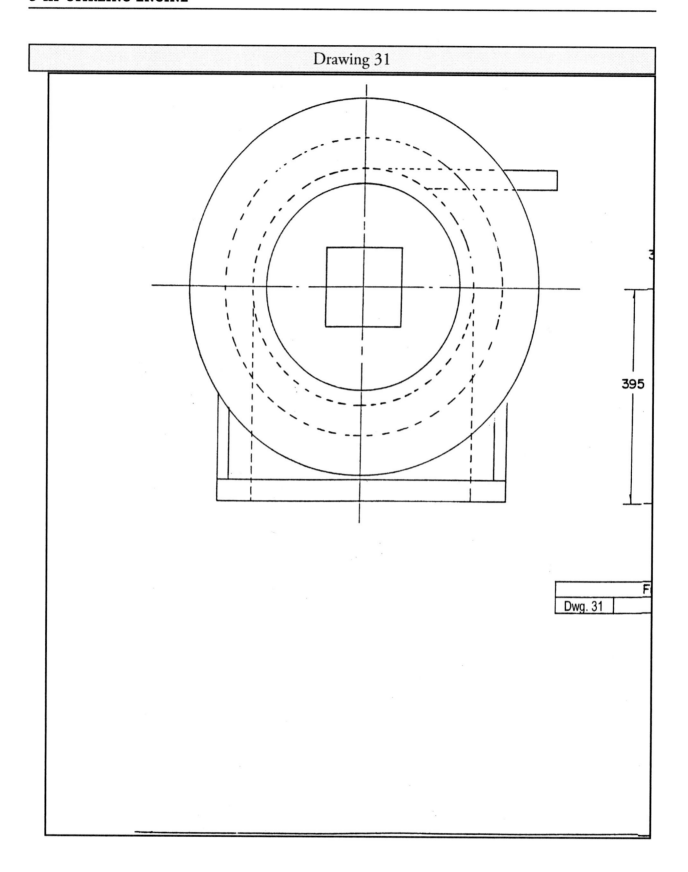

Drawing 31

395

Dwg. 31

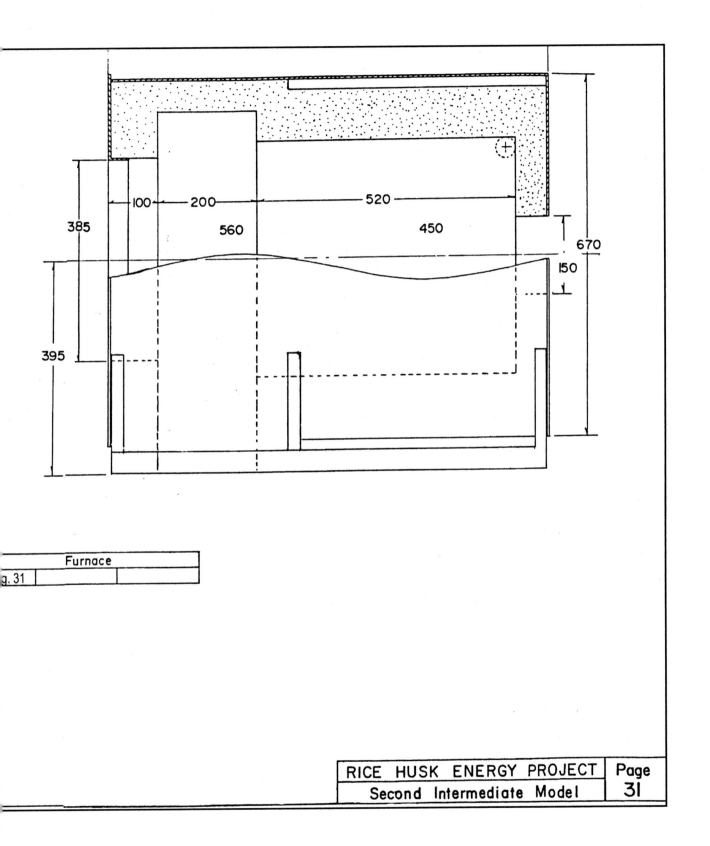

Furnace		
g. 31		

RICE HUSK ENERGY PROJECT	Page
Second Intermediate Model	31

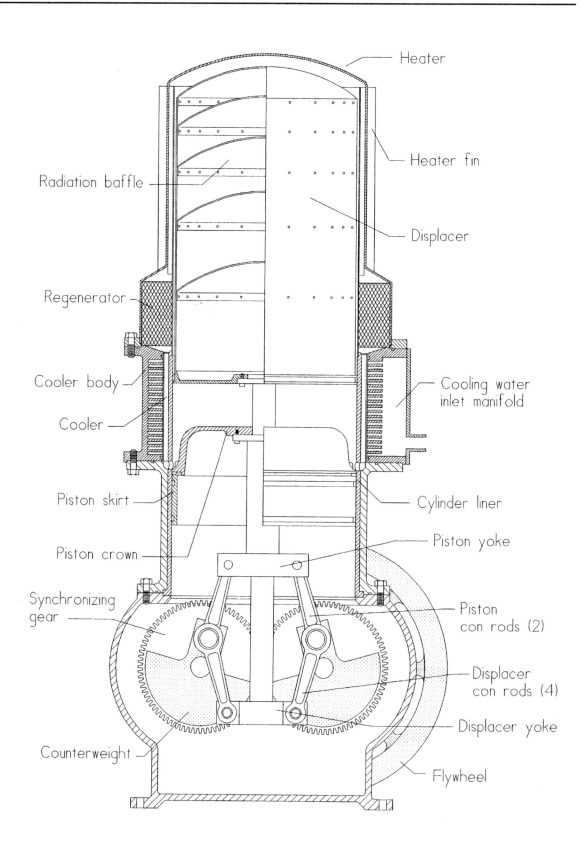

Heater

Heater fin

Radiation baffle

Displacer

Regenerator

Cooler body

Cooling water inlet manifold

Cooler

Piston skirt

Cylinder liner

Piston crown

Piston yoke

Synchronizing gear

Piston con rods (2)

Displacer con rods (4)

Displacer yoke

Counterweight

Flywheel

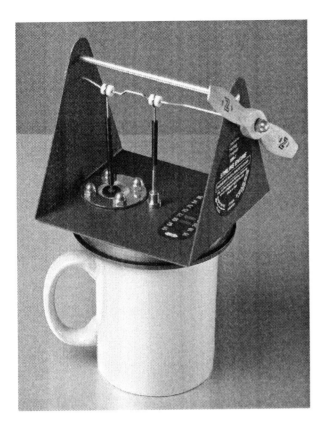

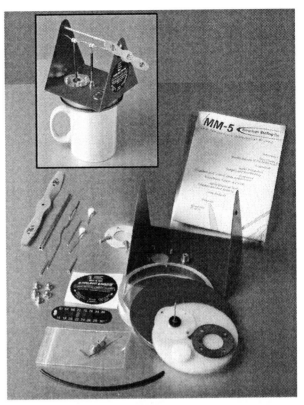

MM-1 Coffee Cup Stirling Engine

Power this engine with a cup of steaming hot coffee or set it on a plate of ice chips (or a bowl of ice cream)to see it run in the opposite direction. The MM-1 has been used for educational demonstrations from middle school science classes to United States Naval Academy thermodynamics classes.

This engine is also a favorite of engineers and techies all over the world! If you need to give a gift to someone who loves technology this is guaranteed to make him happy. The MM-1 comes ready to run and spins about 250 rpm on hot coffee or 100 rpm running on ice.

Our Price: $159.00

MM-5 Coffee Cup Engine Kit

This kit includes all the parts to build our original transparent engine that sells ready to run for $159.00
Ready to assemble. You only need to purchase superglue and silicone sealant. You will also need a few common hand tools. It's a pleasant two or three evening kit and a fun way to learn about Stirling engines.

The United States Naval Academy has their mechanical engineering students build one of our kits.

Our Price: $119.00

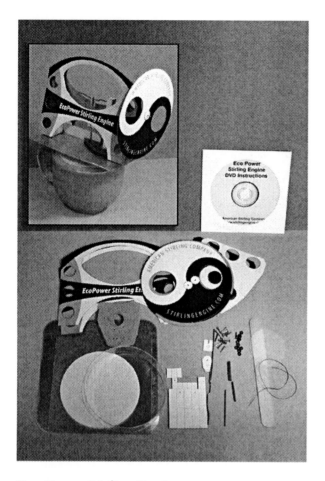

Eco Power Stirling Engine

The Eco Power Stirling engine is a great way to have more fun building a Stirling engine while spending less money.

Precision die cut cardboard and sheetmetal parts, a little epoxy, crazy glue and a few hours give you a working Stirling engine.

It will run off the heat of a mug of hot water for 10 minutes, even more if you tweak it right.

It's our first engine kit to come with a instructional DVD so your engine will go together easier and faster.

Our Price: $49.00

MM-7 Stirling Engine

The amazing MM-7 Stirling engine will run indefinitely on just the heat from your warm hand! As a gift, conversation piece, or classroom demo, you can be sure it will be unique and attention getting.

It will run indefinitely on your warm hands in a 72 degree F (23 degree C) room or on a computer monitor, TV, DVD player, VCR, stereo amplifier/receiver or fax machine. It will even run on bright sunlight shining through a window. It only requires that the base plate be 7.2 degrees F (4 degrees C) warmer or cooler than the top plate. MM-7's now have a laser engraved serial number and logo.

Our Price: $379.00

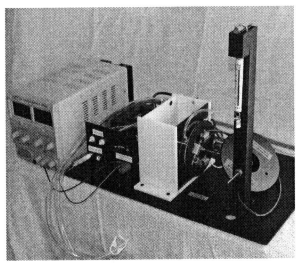

Around the World by Stirling Engine
This book is probably the best general book on Stirling engines. It not only explains how Stirling engines work, it also covers all the current power producing uses of Stirling engines along with how to contact the people who build them.

This book covers everyting from Stirling engines in military submarines, to a Stirling engine that powers the rotisserie for an Oklahoma mechanic's barbecue.

136 pages long and measures 5.5" wide x 8" tall

Our Price: $22.95

Smart Stirling Lab Engine v. 1.5
The Smart Stirling lab engine was developed at the request of University of Kentucky thermodynamics professor Jim Smart.

This engine is intended for physics and thermodynamics professors who want to provide a high-quality lab experience for their students. It comes with pressure, temperature, and volume sensors along with custom electronics and data acquisition software to interface with a PC

The engine was significantly updated in spring 2007. It now includes a built in dynamoter and custom software to make the data acquisition easier.

Our Price: $2495.00

American Stirling Company
beautiful Stirling engines and kits

Welcome to the exciting world of Stirling engines. Here is a small sampling of the products that are available on our website at:
http://www.stirlingengine.com/

Your Chance for Fame! (well sort of)

This book is just a start. We originally wanted to publish a book that would be a complete "How To" manual for building a practical engine like this for home use. Unfortunately Merrick Lockwood had lost some of his original drawings so we didn't have as much detail as we wanted. Besides that, the original engine needed to be changed some before publishing a detailed "How To" manual.

After thinking about it, we decided that it was better to start with a book about a 5 Hp Stirling engine so that some of our customers could get started building the engines that they wanted to build.

So here's your opportunity. Take the ideas from this book and build an engine based on them. Take lots of pictures, and make lots of notes and drawings as you go along because when you are done we want you to be the author of a companion book called, "How You Can Build a 5 Hp. Stirling Engine."

Writing experience is absolutely NOT necessary. We can interview you and actually write and produce the book for you.

So take lots of great pictures and make careful drawings as you build your engine. Try to make your engine as economical and as simple as possible so people can afford to build it. When your engine is running, give us a call at the phone number listed here: http://www.stirlingengine.com/contact-us/

We aren't guaranteeing anything, but when you get your engine running, we really want to talk to you.

Brent H. Van Arsdell
President
American Stirling Company